NEXUS
MEDIA LIMITED

*For Katie, Simon
and Alex*

# GROWING IN ROCKWOOL

Denis Smith  631.585

Grower Manual No 2
2nd Series

**Grower Books**
Nexus Media Limited, Kent

Grower Books
Nexus Media Limited
Nexus House
Swanley, Kent  BR8 8HU

First published 1996

Reprinted in 1998

© Grower Books 1998

ISBN 1 899372 06 7

Series editor Peter Rogers.       Production Octavia Wolton.
Publisher Tony Salter.

Printed in Great Britain.

*Due care has been taken in the preparation of this book. This information is based on standard industry practice as interpreted by the author; it should not be regarded as a complete production programme nor as the only suitable regime. The publisher and author will not accept responsibility for an outcome arising from the application of the information it contains.*

***Publishers' note:*** *'ROCKWOOL' is a trademark belonging to Rockwool International A/S. It is used in the title of this book and throughout with the permission of Rockwool International A/S to whom the publishers are grateful.*

***Cover picture:*** *Rockwool-raised tomato plants set out in the glasshouse [Photograph courtesy of Grodania A/S & Rockwool Grodan BV]*

# Contents

*Abbreviations used in this Manual*

| | | | | | |
|---|---|---|---|---|---|
| AMP | acid magnesium phosphate | g | gram | MJ | megaJoules |
| | | gcal | gram calorie | ml | millilitre |
| CEC | cation exchange capacity | ha | hectare | mm | millimetre |
| | | ISE | ion-selective electrode | mmol | millimoles |
| cf | conductivity factor | | | mS | milliSiemens |
| cm | centimetre | kg | kilogramme | ppm | parts per million |
| cu m | cubic metre | klux | kilolux | sq m | square metre |
| EC | electrical conductivity | meq | milliequivalents | W | Watts |
| | | mg | milligram | µmol | micromoles |

# *Introduction*

When Rockwool in Horticulture, the predecessor to this book, was published in 1987 rockwool was by far the most important inert horticultural substrate although even then there was a lot of interest in alternative manufactured materials. Perlite, for example, was already popular in Scotland and the north of England, while Belgian growers were starting to move into polyurethane foam. Materials such as pumice and expanded clay aggregates had their devotees and glasswool was already being developed as an alternative fibre for slabs.

There have been many changes in the way rockwool and other substrates have been used since 1987. The most far-reaching has been the move away from open, free-draining systems into 'closed systems'. Rockwool first appeared as a horticultural substrate as an extension of nutrient film technique (NFT) and it was therefore used exclusively in closed recirculating systems. By 1987 NFT growers had abandoned this approach in favour of free-draining installations because closed systems had too many problems with the build-up of salts and diseases in the root environment. At that time there were no obvious benefits to compensate for these problems. More recently, however, intense environmental pressures have served to force a switch back into isolated growing systems. The search for economic and effective closed growing systems began in earnest around 1990.

These changes have been most dramatically evident in Holland, where in the mid-1990s growers faced being allowed to produce crops *only* in totally contained growing systems effectively isolated from the environment. By 1991 more than 500ha of glass in Holland had already switched to closed systems. This switch was only the first stage in satisfying the needs of the environmental lobby, however, because in most cases although the drainage from the substrate was collected it was dumped rather than recirculated.

Since then many of the problems inherent in total containment and recirculation have been solved, although at a substantial cost to the grower. The build-up of salts can be minimised by making as much use as possible of high quality water sources like rainwater, and it can be completely eliminated by installing water treatment equipment using techniques like reverse osmosis or cation exchange resins. The loss of nutrient balance which is inevitable in a recirculating system can be managed by using a more flexible fertiliser injection system. The problems of disease spread can be overcome by drainage solution sterilisation, using heat, UV light or ozone sterilisation.

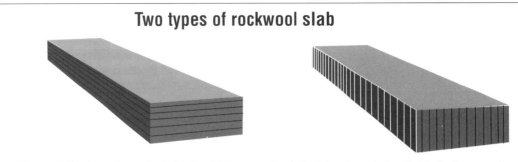

## Two types of rockwool slab

**The original rockwool slabs had fibres orientated horizontally (left). Later versions orientated the fibres vertically and changed the slab's water-holding characteristics**

sterilisation. Since the system is raised off the ground the root zone temperature can be manipulated to maximise growth. The water requirement of the crop does not need to be calculated, the crop simply takes what it needs and the deficit in the system volume is made up automatically.

With hindsight the next development was obvious. What was needed was a growing system which retains all the advantages of NFT but which holds the root system in an environment in which the balance between air and water can more easily be kept at its optimum level.

### Rockwool makes a timely arrival

Rockwool appeared on the scene just at the right time. In fact the use of rockwool as a substrate was being developed and tried in the early 1970's in Denmark, but it was towards the end of the decade before it had moved into Holland and from there to the UK and elsewhere. Rockwool was quickly recognised as the missing link in NFT, a rooting material which could be freely watered and drained, yet which could be managed to provide an optimum ratio between air and water in the root zone.

Through the efforts and expertise of Grodania A/S, the Danish company which first developed rockwool as a horticultural substrate, rockwool slabs were soon tried and proved throughout Europe for many different horticultural crops. More recently the extensive use of rockwool has spread further afield, to the main horticultural centres of North America, Australasia and the Far East.

Over this period of time rockwool has by no means been a static product. As experience was gained with an increasing range of crops and growing conditions, manufacturing techniques were adapted to fine tune the characteristics of the rockwool slabs to meet the growers' specifications. First came the so-called vertical fibre slab, in which the orientation of the fibre structure was changed to alter the distribution pattern of water applied to the surface of the slab and to change its water-holding characteristics. Then came the low density slab, a more economical product with a slightly lower air to water ratio but with a shorter useful life. More recently still, the variable density slab has appeared, making it possible to customise water distribution, drainage and aeration through the depth of the slab to suit the requirements of particular crops.

### Alternatives to rockwool

As rockwool took hold in Europe other substrates were being tried and adopted in some production areas. Glasswool slabs were developed as an alternative to rockwool (see chapter 6, p35). They proved to have slightly different physical characteristics and may offer better prospects for disposal at the end of their useful life. Perlite (chapter 3, p14), which had been around for many years mainly as an additive in peat-based potting composts, was made into an isolated growing system for tomatoes and other crops (this was largely due to the efforts of the West of Scotland Agricultural College at Auchincruive and the use of perlite growing systems is still centred around that area). Polyurethane foam waste from the furniture industry, chipped and bonded into slabs, was being developed in Belgium, where it is still widely used (chapter 5, p23). Pumice (chapter 4, p19), expanded clay aggregates (p36) and other materials have all found their champions, often in areas where a surplus of the material has led to a search for ways of making use of it.

The substrates picture is more complicated now than it has ever been. Rockwool certainly still holds centre stage, and will do so for many years. The research and experience which has gone into rockwool will keep its value for a long time, even supposing there are few further possible improvements to its structural development. The fact that Part 3 of this book focusses solely on rockwool is evidence of the massive volume of expertise which has been accumulated on the use of this substrate over the last 20 years. But there is a lot of research and commercial effort being put into many of the less universally used substrates, much of this inspired by the success of rockwool, and this will at least ensure their survival in the short term.

It is difficult to be convinced that any of the alternative substrates described here will ever challenge the overall superiority of rockwool. Certainly some of these materials will hold their own in limited geographical areas or for particular cropping systems, particularly where a granulate material is more suitable than a slab material, but they do not appear to have the potential to take over from rockwool on a worldwide scale. It is of course possible that an as yet unconsidered substrate will appear on the scene to challenge the supremacy of rockwool, but for the moment it looks as though it will continue to be the mainstay of substrate growing for many years.

The principal substrates in use or under development today can be broadly grouped into three categories according to the type of system in which they are most commonly used (see panel). The first category, of which rockwool is the obvious example, is mainly used in structured form such as

## Categories of substrates

| | |
|---|---|
| SLABS &BLOCKS | Rockwool |
| | Polyurethane foam |
| | Glasswool |
| | Duroplast foam |
| | |
| INDIVIDUAL CONTAINERS | Perlite |
| | Expanded clay aggregates |
| | Pumice |
| | Zeolites |
| | Slagwool |
| | Rockwool granulates & |
| | special mixes |
| | |
| OPEN TROUGHS | Expanded clay aggregates |
| | Pumice |
| | Washed river sand |

Soms substrates also have uses in categories for which they are not listed growing slabs and blocks. The second category comprises materials generally contained in plastic 'pillows' or bags. The third category includes materials generally contained in open troughs of various kinds. Materials in the first category are bonded or moulded, the other two are granulate materials.

## THE ADVANTAGES OF SUBSTRATES

Several advantages of using substrates have already been mentioned in passing. The most obvious one is that substrates take the crop out of the glasshouse border soil. Unlikely though it may seem, soil is not really a suitable rooting medium for intensive horticulture. Its structure is variable and difficult to maintain crop after crop, so maintaining an adequate supply of oxygen to the roots while allowing the crop free access to as much water and nutrients as it requires is not easy.

Soil is often colder than the glasshouse atmosphere. This limits the growth of the root system and slows down the development of the crop. Heating a large volume of soil is possible but costly.

Soil is also an excellent medium for the growth of fungal and other diseases which inevitably become established in an intensive cropping programme. Attempting to eliminate them completely by soil sterilisation is very difficult as well as being expensive and time-consuming.

Substrates like rockwool translate all of the disadvantages of soil into advantages. They allow fine control of the supply of oxygen, water and nutrients to the roots. They are lightweight, quick to warm up and can be economically heated to the optimum requirements of the crop. They are initially sterile, and in most cases they can be sterilised for re-use more cheaply and effectively than soil.

The advantages of using substrates rather than growing in the soil have been widely demonstrated, particularly in the case of rockwool. Even first-time users, who inevitably make mistakes and often fail to take full advantage of a substrate system in the first season, report substantial yield and quality improvements as well as more consistent crop management. These gains usually result in an increase in financial returns which is more than enough to justify the cost of the switch into substrate growing. Few growers who move out of the soil would ever consider moving back.

The extra cost of establishing and running a substrate growing system, although it is likely to be quickly recovered, should not be underestimated. The irrigation and fertilisation equipment which is needed for substrates is a major capital cost for most new installations, while the higher running costs incurred in purchasing the substrate and increased amounts of fertilisers and good quality water can be considerable. Even the labour input can be higher for substrate crops, with more vigorous growth and a longer production season, but since a large part of the additional labour is needed to harvest the increased crop yield it is not difficult to justify its cost.

### ROCKWOOL IN NORTH AMERICA

Interest in the use of rockwool increased rapidly in the 1980's in both Canada and the USA. Some of the growing techniques described here need modification to take account of the wider range of environmental conditions encountered in North America. These, and the problem of differences in terminology and units of measurement between Europe and North America, are addressed in the Appendix (p129).

# 2 Rockwool

*How rockwool is made. Its characteristics. Propagating in rockwool. Its advantages and requirements. Its granulate form.*

Rockwool — which is sometimes referred to as stonewool — is manufactured from a basaltic or similar diabasic rock. The crushed rock is mixed with coke and the mixture heated beyond its melting point to a temperature of 1,500C or above. The molten material is then spun into fibres by pouring it on to a series of discs spinning at high speed. The length and thickness of the fibres — important factors in determining the physical characteristics of the finished product — are controlled mainly by the melt temperature and the speed at which the discs spin.

Before the molten rock is fed to the discs it is combined with additives, which include carbonate of lime, a wetting agent and, for slab production, organic resin to bind the fibres together. The resin is usually phenol-based, a material which is related to the plastic bakelite. Other materials are added to ensure the water absorbency or repellency of the finished product. Rockwool for horticultural use is generally water absorbant, although the water repellent form (more commonly used as an insulating material in the building trade) is also used in granulate form as a constituent of compost mixes or as a soil amendment material.

The bonding agent is fundamental to the structural stability of rockwool slabs and blocks. The strength and distribution of bonding links between the fibres determines how long the material will retain its structural integrity, whether it can be steam sterilised, and how many times in can be re-used without losing too much of its structure. All standard density rockwool slabs currently available have been shown to retain their structure adequately for seven years or more for a single long-term crop such as roses, or to withstand reuse for at least three annual crops with steam sterilisation between each crop. Lower density slabs have a shorter useful life, but even they can be steam sterilised and re-used at least once if they are handled with care.

Once the fibres have been spun and they have started to cool they are formed either into a loose flock or granulate, or compressed and moulded under controlled conditions to form slabs. The slabs can then be cut up to produce smaller blocks, cubes or plugs. These formed products are wrapped or sleeved as required and can then be further manipulated to incorporate planting holes or other features.

The distribution and orientation of the fibres in the finished product is determined during the manufacturing process. At one time the fibre orientation was mainly random, but with a tendency to run horizontally. A few years ago it was shown that better drainage and increased aeration could be achieved in a slab with a predominantly vertical fibre orientation, so many bonded rockwool products are now based on vertical fibre orientation (see p4).

### Characteristics of bonded rockwool

Bonded rockwool products — slabs, blocks, cubes and plugs — can be manufactured in a range of densities by varying the pressure under which the fibres are extruded. The standard density a few years ago was 70 to 80kg/cu m, and this is still the most popular grade. However lower density products are available. These are slightly less expensive per unit volume, because they contain less material and are intended for relatively short-term production such as single season vegetable crops, although they can sometimes be sterilised and reused for a limited period if they are handled with care.

The lower density material tends to hold less water and more air at full capacity than the standard product. This is seldom a problem except in a few specific situations, but it has to be taken into account in crop management. Smaller blocks and cubes should always be made from high density rockwool to ensure their structural integrity and a stable air to water ratio.

A wide range of bonded products is available for horticultural use. The major supplier worldwide is the Danish company Grodania A/S, but rockwool products are also available from several other European manufacturers, including Cultilene and Basalan. Growing slabs, usually between 80 and 120cm in length, can be 7.5, 10 or 15cm deep, with a width of between 10 and 30cm. The width of the slab is chosen to suit the glasshouse layout and the crop planting arrangement. The most popular depth of slab is 7.5cm, and the higher cost of deeper slabs seldom gives a worthwhile benefit for the major horticultural crops. Apart from the choice of high or low fibre density and of horizontal or vertical fibre orientation (p4), slabs can be obtained either unwrapped or wrapped in a polyethylene sleeve, either singly or in pairs. The most popular slab for vegetable production is 7.5cm deep and 15cm wide, with a vertical fibre orientation.

### Rockwool slabs — the options

The most popular sizes and grades of rockwool slabs at the time of writing are:

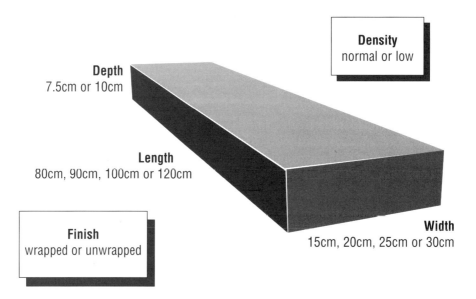

**Density** normal or low

**Depth** 7.5cm or 10cm

**Length** 80cm, 90cm, 100cm or 120cm

**Width** 15cm, 20cm, 25cm or 30cm

**Finish** wrapped or unwrapped

A more recent option is the graded fibre density slab. This has a closer mesh at the top of the slab and a more open structure towards the bottom. This slab is claimed to be particularly suitable for cut flower crops because it provides a more uniform water distribution through the slab and reduces the risk of over-irrigation when the crop is growing less actively. The denser material close to the surface of the slab encourages better lateral spread of nutrient solution away from the point of irrigation, while the more open structure towards the base improves the drainage and gives better aeration lower down in the slab. The end result is that suitable conditions for root development can be found through a larger proportion of the slab volume, which is therefore used more efficiently.

## Propagating in rockwool — the options

One major advantage of rockwool as a growing medium is that it can be produced in many different forms according to the requirements of the crop and growing system. For example there is a wide range of plugs, small cubes and larger blocks for germinating seed, rooting cuttings, establishing micropropagated plants and for the later stages of plant propagation. Specialist products include capillary matting, thin slabs or strips for growing aquatic plants or herbs and granulate growing mixes for interior landscaping containers.

The more commonly used sizes of plugs, cubes and blocks for plant propagation are shown in the panel. Not all available options are included.

### Propagation options

*PLUGS*
   Cylindrical plugs in polystyrene trays
   2 x 2 x 2.7cm deep — 240/tray

*CUBES*
   Individual 'cubes', cylindrical or conical profile
   2.5 x 2.5 x 4cm deep — 150/tray
   3.6 x 3.6 x 4cm deep — 77/tray

*MINIBLOCKS*
   Individual cubes wrapped in strips
   5 x 5 x 4cm deep

*MULTIBLOCKS*
   Cubes joined at the top to form mats
   2.5 x 2.5 x 4cm deep — 200/mat
   3.6 x 3.6 x 4cm deep — 98/mat

*PROPAGATION BLOCKS*
   Individually wrapped blocks, with or without grooved bases
   7.5 x 7.5 x 6.5 or 10cm deep
   10 x 10 x 6.5cm deep

## Air/water distribution

The most important feature of rockwool, and that which has made the biggest contribution to the rate at which rockwool has been accepted commercially, is that it is easy to keep an optimal balance between air and water within its structure. This means that the crop will never suffer water stress either from dryness or from waterlogging, nor will it be deprived of oxygen. It is not impossible to produce an unfavourable root environment in rockwool, but with reasonable horticultural skills it is certainly very difficult.

A typical rockwool slab consists of only about 5% of fibres and 95% of pore space. When water is added to a free-draining rockwool slab it will drain down to a particular level, and leave both air and water within this pore space. A slab which has been watered to capacity and allowed to drain freely from the base will end up with a water content of around 65% and an air content of around 30%, although the actual figures will depend on factors like fibre density, slab height, fibre orientation and slab slope. So a 10 litre slab will contain more than six litres of water after irrigation.

The air and water is not distributed uniformly through the slab. There will obviously be a higher proportion of water in the base of the slab and more air towards the top once conditions have stabilised following each irrigation cycle. The distribution pattern of air and water within the slab is used by the crop to allow it to develop a root system throughout that part of the total volume which has the best balance for that crop. Many crops develop coarser water-seeking roots either on or close to the base of the slab, and a finer root structure above. If the density of fibres within the slab is graded from top to bottom as described on p9, the distribution of air and water within the slab volume can be further improved.

Whatever type of slab is used, the bulk of the root system of most crops will be found within a limited part of the total slab volume, in the region where conditions are optimal for root growth. This is not a problem, but it does mean that the management of the slabs should not change in such a way as, for example, to raise or lower the water table suddenly. If this happens the existing root system will suffer, and the development of the crop will be checked until new root can be formed in a more acceptable part of the slab.

The availability of water in a rockwool slab, and the ease with which it can be extracted by the crop, is substantially greater than for most other horticultural growing media. In soil or peat, the effort required to pull water out of the medium increases considerably as the water content decreases. This means that however carefully the crop is irrigated there will be occasions when the plants are under water stress. With rockwool this effect is very much less, and approximately 90% of the total water capacity of a slab can be extracted by the crop before there is any significant increase in resistance. This produces better crop growth, although it does have the disadvantage that the plants produce a relatively small root volume, because they do not need to explore the substrate extensively to maximise their water uptake. This is acceptable if the conditions within the slab are static, but it can be a problem if the growing conditions within the colonised volume of the slab become less favourable.

## THE ADVANTAGES OF ROCKWOOL

Rockwool has many advantages for the grower, six in particular:

- It has a large pore capacity for air and water
- It retains a good balance between air and water content
- It is chemically inert
- It is structurally stable and consistent in quality
- It contains no pathogens
- It can be sterilised by steam and re-used

The limited volume in a rockwool slab means that there is a low buffering capacity for water and nutrients, so the hydraulic properties of rockwool are an important factor in assessing how, and even if, a particular type of slab should be used as a horticultural substrate.

Israeli growers are expected to use rockwool as a substrate increasingly over the next decade, and research at the Hebrew University of Jerusalem has been aimed at defining and measuring the most important hydraulic properties of different types of rockwool slabs. Water retention curves during both wetting and drying cycles are seen as a must in this type of work, and these now often make an appearance in manufacturers' promotional material. At the present time it seems that the physical characteristics of rockwool slabs from the principal European manufacturers, while showing some marginal differences, are similar enough to make any of them suitable for most situations provided they are managed approriately.

If a rockwool crop is watered in such a way that it never contains less than 15% water, or about a quarter of what it contains immediately after generous irrigation, then the crop will never suffer from lack of water if it has a sound and active root system. If the slabs are free-draining at the base the crop will never suffer waterlogging, because within a few minutes of irrigation the rockwool will once again contain around 30% air.

Despite these major advantages in rockwool a lot of effort has gone into refining irrigation techniques and monitoring methods to ensure that the air and water balance in the substrate is as close to optimum as possible. These techniques are discussed in chapter 9 and more information is given in the chapters covering individual crops.

## REQUIREMENTS FOR ROCKWOOL GROWING

While rockwool, in common with other materials, is an excellent substrate for most horticultural crops, it can only be reliably used as an alternative to soil if certain facilities are available. Probably the most important of these is a source of good quality water in sufficient quantities for the demands of the crop throughout the year. The volume of water needed at any particular time can be very substantial, especially in the summer months. A guide to the month-by-month water requirements of a typical glasshouse crop is given in chapter 8.

### Water quality

Water which contains a high level of dissolved salts is not ideal even for soil crops, but for rockwool it is usually disastrous. The problem is worst in recirculating systems, where the salt content builds up rapidly and soon restricts the growth of the crop. Even in an open free-draining installation poor quality water makes crop management in rockwool difficult.

The first option to consider is rainwater. This contains no dissolved salts so it is ideal for use with rockwool, either used alone or blended with a less suitable source of water. If good quality water is not available then the possibility of water treatment to remove a proportion of the dissolved salts has to be considered. Alternative ways of treating water are discussed in chapter 8.

### Nutrition

Another essential requirement for rockwool growing is the ability to provide a complete nutrient solution to the crop continuously. Unlike soils, which usually provide a background source of nutrients like calcium, phosphorus and most of the essential trace elements, rockwool is completely inert and offers nothing to the crop at all. There are several ways to prepare and deliver a correctly formulated nutrient solution to the crop, ranging from the relatively simple but inflexible one tank mix to multi-tank computer controlled installations. These are discussed in chapter 11.

Depending on the quality of the water it may also be necessary to provide acidity regulation equipment either separately or as a part of the fertiliser incorporation facilities. With a particularly consistent source of water it may be possible to do this just by adding a suitable acid into the stock tanks, but this option carries an increased risk of over-acidification.

### Precision irrigation

A third 'must' is an accurate and reliable drip irrigation system. The demands for precision irrigation in rockwool are much greater than for an equivalent crop grown in the soil. The plants are grown in small isolated units, often only two or three to a single slab, so it is important to know that every slab is receiving the same volume of nutrient solution at every irrigation. This is not easily achieved, especially when application volumes as low as 50 ml/plant may be used. The design, operation and maintenance of the irrigation system is a major factor in successful rockwool growing.

# Rockwool granulates

In addition to slab or block form, rockwool is available in an unbonded form described as granulate or flock, in coarse, medium or fine grades, ranging from more than 15 litres/kg for the coarsest product down to less than 7 litres/kg. Average particle size of the fine material is around 3 to 6mm diameter. Both water repellent and water absorbent versions are produced; intermediate absorbency can be achieved by Imixing the two. Water absorbent rockwool granulate is mainly used as a potting compost. The water repellent form is most widely used for soil conditioning.

Once a lot of plants were raised in rockwool granulate instead of today's more common plugs and cubes.

Some growers prefer to use containers of rockwool granulate. For this purpose the best material is a mixture of repellent and absorbent medium grade granulate. A few crops of gerberas, freesias, cymbidiums and anthuriums are grown in this mix, which is also used by some plant raisers for tomatoes and cucumbers. A range of pre-mixed and pH-buffered products is available for crops like orchids. Water absorbent medium grade granulate is also used on a small scale in amenity horticulture, particularly as a lightweight substrate for hanging baskets.

The nutritional requirements of crops in rockwool granulates are the same as those for bonded rockwool. The material is chemically inert, although unbuffered granulates tend to have a higher starting pH which has to be taken into account for a short time when new material is first used. The rules for irrigation are also similar, although the high water holding capacity of shallow depth mixes containing a high proportion of water absorbent granulate make it especially important to ensure good drainage from the base of the containers.

The container depth can be adjusted to get the optimum air to water ratio in the granulate for any particular purpose. For example a 5cm depth of medium grade material will hold 75% water and 20% air, while a 20cm depth of the same grade will hold only 55% water and 40% air.

## Advice and support

Finally the availability of technical support should not be ignored, especially for the newcomer to substrates. Advice and local experience can be easily obtained in an intensive and technologically advanced horticultural centre like the Westland of Holland, but it will be a lot more difficult to find almost anywhere else.

The expertise of the rockwool manufacturers and their distributors should not be passed over in these circumstances. They have a professional interest in making sure that their product performs well wherever it is used, and they have an unparallelled source of experience to draw on.

Analytical support will also be needed for routine substrate analysis. Again this is no problem in some areas, but in isolated situations the rockwool supplier may once again be the best bet.

## PREPARING FOR ROCKWOOL

Two major advantages of rockwool — its initial freedom from soil-borne pathogens and its ability to provide an optimum air to water ratio in the root zone — can only be used effectively if the glasshouse is properly prepared and set out.

The crop and substrate should always be completely isolated from the glasshouse floor. This is usually done by laying an adequate thickness of polyethylene sheet over the soil surface with plenty of overlap.

If the overlaps are positioned in shallow depressions between each pair of crop rows any drainage solution or residual water from crop spraying will be removed from the surface. This is more important in a free-draining system than in a closed installation. Various types of installation are described in detail in chapter 7.

Even if the rockwool slabs are positioned off the floor in channels or on benches, covering the floor is still necessary to prevent any root disease organisms being transferred into the substrate. The longer the crop is to remain in situ, the more attention should be given to isolating it.

Before the floor is covered it is necessary to carry out any levelling or contouring. This is particularly important when slabs are placed directly on the floor, although it is also necessary to ensure the right slope for drainage channels or gullies. The drainage characteristics of rockwool are such that only a very slight slope either along or across the width of each slab is needed to avoid undrained areas within the substrate and to carry unwanted drainage solution away. A greater slope does not produce any further advantage, and reduces the useful volume of the substrate by limiting the area over which the optimum air to water ratio can be provided.

Equally important for optimum drainage is that all slabs, whether wrapped or open, should be free to drain from the bottom of their lower edge. Unlike some other substrate systems, rockwool is not normally set up to provide a sump of nutrient solution in the base of each slab. The effect of doing this would be to reduce the useful volume of the slab.

# 3 Perlite

*The manufacture of perlite. Its characteristics. Propagation and growing techniques. Practical experience.*

Perlite is produced from a volcanic aluminosilicate rock similar to pumice, which is first crushed and then heated to a temperature of a little below 1,000C. At this temperature the water and gas which is trapped within the structure of the crushed rock vaporises to expand the particles rather like popcorn, producing a very light aerated white mineral foam. The individual granules, which range in size from dust to about 6mm, and which have a rough irregular surface, contain numerous closed air-filled cells.

Like most of the substrates now used in horticulture, perlite was first developed for industrial purposes, in this case as a lightweight insulating material for the building industry. Perlite has actually been used in horticulture for many years, much longer than most of the other substrates. As long ago as the 1960's it was a popular constituent of potting composts, particularly of the 'peat-lite' mixes developed in the USA. It is still widely used as an ingredient of potting compost mixes, usually in combination with peat or vermiculite.

It is important that perlite should not be confused with vermiculite, which not only has quite different physical characteristics such as its water holding capacity, but also has a very considerable cation exchange capacity (see chapter 1). This means that, unlike perlite, vermiculite has a considerable influence on the nutritional behaviour of any mix in which it is included.

## Characteristics of perlite

Perlite is very light, with a bulk density of around 100kg/cu m, or about one twentieth the weight of sand. The individual granules vary in diameter up to 6mm or more, but the grades used in horticulture are usually within the range 1.5 to 4.5mm.

It is important that the average granule size of horticultural grade perlite should not be too small. A trial carried out on tomatoes at Auchincruive in 1988 showed that a fine grade perlite failed to match the performance of coarser grades, probably because it retained too much moisture. If at least 50% of the granules have a diameter of 1.5mm or above there should be no problem, although finer grades may still be acceptable if the depth of the nutrient solution reservoir is reduced to no more than about 2 or 3cm.

The extensive pore spaces contained within perlite granules are closed, so they are not generally available to accept or distribute water within the substrate. The available water is actually held on and between the irregular surfaces of adjacent granules. The rough external surface of the granules is mainly responsible for the considerable capillary attraction which perlite has for water.

Perlite has a negligible cation exchange capacity, so it is more genuinely inert than many of the other substrates which are considered here. It has a nominal pH of around 7.0 to 7.5, but this is of little practical significance since the material has no substantial effect on the pH of the nutrient solution held within its volume. The individual granules are strong enough to resist some compression without fracturing, so the substrate can be re-used several times without any major change in its physical characteristics. It is resistant to steam temperatures, so it can be sterilised as necessary, either in situ or in bulk steaming bins.

## GROWING TECHNIQUES WITH PERLITE

The development of perlite for soilless crop production can be largely credited to the West of Scotland Agricultural College at Auchincruive. When perlite was first considered as a substrate for tomato production it was used in large 60 litre sausage-shaped bags, each containing six plants which were individually irrigated with drip nozzles. This approach was soon modified so that smaller 20 to 30 litre bags, about 90cm long, could be positioned on each side of the heating pipes with three plants in each. In both cases the key to success proved to be providing a shallow sump in the base of each container from which nutrient solution could be drawn by taking advantage of the strong capillary action of the substrate.

Provided a reservoir of nutrient solution is maintained at all times the water content of the perlite at any particular height above the reservoir will remain constant whatever the demands of the crop. For example, at a height of 2cm above the free water level in the reservoir the water content will be about 50%. At heights of 4, 6, 8 and 10cm above the reservoir the water content will be around 49%, 48%, 46% and 44% respectively. The capillarity of perlite is so strong that even at a height of 15 cm above the reservoir the water content of the substrate will usually be at least 35%. This means that the crop will have a uniform and ample supply of water at all times and will never suffer from water stress so long as the reservoir is always topped up.

### Gullies and reservoirs

A suitable depth of reservoir can be achieved in either of two ways. The individual bags, with drainage slits down to the base, can be put into polyethylene lined gullies which run along the length of the row and which are constructed to form and maintain a reservoir around the bags.

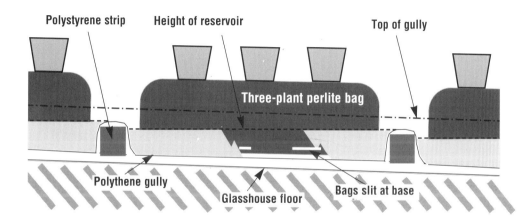

Alternatively the individual bags can be placed out directly and slit horizontally at a height of 3 to 4 cm above the base. The optimum depth of the reservoir depends on the grade of perlite. An exceptionally coarse grade will benefit from a 4 or 5cm reservoir, while 2 to 3cm is better if the perlite contains a lot of finer material.

The gulley option is a closed system so that any nutrient imbalances will be magnified over a period of time and any salt accumulation will also be accentuated. It is therefore only suitable for good quality water supplies. If there is a slope along the rows it is necessary to build dams into the system to ensure that each bag in the gulley has a reservoir in its base. This is done by inserting a 3 to 4cm high strip of polystyrene underneath the polyethylene gulley between each bag. If the slope along the row is very small it is enough to insert a dam after every second or third bag, while for a perfectly level row there may be no need for dams at all. The polyethylene sheet which forms the gulley is then taken up over the top of the growing bags to isolate the reservoir from the glasshouse.

### Heating and irrigation

Root zone heating is achieved with a perlite growing bag system by running a heating pipe loop either under the bags or under the gulley. In either case the heating loop should be set on to a polystyrene slab to insulate the system from the glasshouse floor.

Perlite systems are generally irrigated by placing drip nozzles into the top of each bag, but in the case of the gulley layout another option is to put the nutrient solution directly into the gulley at its top end to replenish all the reservoirs along the row. Capillary action will then supply the substrate from each reservoir. If the crop is irrigated only from the end of each row it is important to always apply enough volume to carry over the dams to reach the far end of the row. If the volume is inadequate it will lead to substantial variation in nutrient status and solution conductivity along the row.

### Propagation

Vegetable crops such as tomatoes, peppers and cucumbers which are to be planted into perlite can be propagated in rockwool cubes, but it is necessary to manage the establishment phase with particular care. This is because the unusually strong capillarity of the perlite can draw so much nutrient solution out of the rockwool that it can be difficult to keep the rockwool cubes adequately moist until the roots have moved down into the perlite. Thoroughly wetting the perlite before planting is obviously important, but it is not enough to avoid the problem of drying out. It is necessary to apply very frequent small volumes of solution to the plants to keep the cubes constantly wet until establishment is complete.

An alternative which has been successfully introduced in Scotland is to raise the plants in perlite in large lattice-base pots with a capacity of about one litre. Seed is germinated in perlite in trays, and the seedlings are moved on shortly after emergence into the lattice pots which have previously been wetted with the nutrient solution which will be used after planting. The lattice pots are stood in large polyethylene lined trays to form a shallow reservoir so that the substrate can be kept moist but not over-wet.

### Monitoring in perlite

Substrate sampling techniques for perlite, in common with other granulate materials, are rather different to those which are used for rockwool and other slabs. For routine day to day monitoring of the solution conductivity and pH it is adequate to draw solution out of the reservoir. One way of doing this is to set a number of 2 to 3cm diameter tubes into the system with their bases in the reservoir, and to use a syringe to draw a small volume of solution out of the bottom of each for testing. At least 12 to 15 sampling points are needed to ensure a reasonably representative reading.

The conductivity of the reservoir solution will generally be about 1.0mS/cm below that of the solution held within the root zone, and the nutrient balance within it will also be quite different. For full analysis it is important to sample directly from the substrate in the root zone rather than from the reservoirs. This is done by extracting small samples of perlite from the root zone and combining these into a bulk sample from which the nutrient solution can be extracted for analysis.

## Reuse of perlite

Perlite can be used for a number of successive crops if it is sterilised each time before re-use. While there is some evidence that crop performance may not always be as high with re-used and untreated perlite as it is with new material, steam sterilisation may actually increase yields over those which are achieved with new perlite. This effect has also been observed with some other substrates.

Various sterilisation options are available with steam being the most popular as well as probably the most effective. Because perlite is so easily handled it is generally steam sterilised in bulk outside the crop area. Unlike slab substrates, with perlite it is relatively easy to remove the bulk of the root system of the old crop before sterilisation.

## PRACTICAL EXPERIENCE

*Tomatoes*    Most of the grower experience with perlite growing systems has come from the tomato sector, mainly in Scotland and the north of England, where it has been used in up to 20 ha of glass. In commercial use a volume of about 6 litres of perlite is allocated to each plant although tomato crops can be grown in volumes as low as 4 litres/plant (three plants in a 12 litre bag) without any loss of production but this calls for a particularly accurate and reliable irrigation system.

*Cucumber and peppers*    Cucumbers and peppers have been successfully grown in similar perlite bag systems. In the case of cucumbers a substrate volume of 6 to 8 litres/plant may give better results than smaller volumes, although this is not certain. A trial with peppers in 1988 allowed a generous 12 litres of perlite per plant, although it is likely that this could be substantially reduced for commercial production with careful irrigation management. Comparisons of vegetable crop performance in perlite and in rockwool have generally shown no consistent differences between the two substrates.

*Cut flowers*    Several cut flower crops have been grown in perlite without any problems, notably alstroemerias, carnations and gerberas. Carnations performed particularly well in perlite in an experimental comparison with rockwool, in both cases using root zone warming to maintain a temperature of around 21C in the substrate. Two carnation varieties planted into perlite at a density of 16 plants/60 litre bag outyielded a rockwool crop planted at 46 plants/sq m of rockwool slab surface by a substantial margin.

*Hardy woody ornamentals*    Perlite is also being tested as a substrate for the production of hardy woody ornamentals in containers, either alone or in combination with fine vermiculite. Trials at the Scottish Agricultural College have shown that either fine or coarse perlite, amended with lime and resin coated controlled release fertilisers, can be used to produce saleable quality plants of non-ericaceous species, and that the quality generally matches that achieved with peat-based media. With ericaceous subjects the results have so far been less successful, though.

Perlite may also prove to be a useful alternative to peat for indoor pot plant production, following some promising trials with Ficus.

# Orchids in Canada

Excellent results have been obtained in Canada using perlite in a reservoir system to grow orchids. One less obvious advantage of perlite to emerge during commercial trials was that the roots could be easily extracted from the perlite and washed clean for examination.

The system now in use in British Columbia is based on 3mm graded perlite with the finer material removed by flotation. The crops are grown in individual containers with either external or integral reservoirs. A 20cm depth of perlite, including a 4cm reservoir, is covered with a thin layer of gravel to improve the stability of the containers.

Orchid seedlings are planted into the containers and irrigated at a very low conductivity at first, using very high quality water and aiming for a total conductivity no higher that 0.3mS/cm. This is then gradually built up to around 1.0mS/cm as the plants become established. With this system sampling the nutrient solution in the reservoir has been found to be an acceptable way of monitoring the nutrition of the crop. After four years of production there was no evidence of any disease establishment nor of any physical deterioration of the perlite.

A direct comparison between the same orchid species grown in either perlite or rockwool produced no recordable differences in performance.

# 4 Pumice

*Production and characteristics of pumice as a growing media. Growing techniques and systems. Practical experience.*

Pumice is produced by volcanic activity. It is an aluminosilicate rock which contains some potassium and sodium but no significant amounts of calcium or magnesium. It is forced up through the earth's crust under pressure to reach the surface as a molten rock which contains a small proportion of water. As the pressure under which it is forced to the surface is released the water vaporises as steam, and the steam in turn expands the solidifying rock. The end product is a light, porous material which, suitably graded, makes a clean and relatively inert horticultural substrate. Pumice rock is itself the starting material for the production of perlite, which is achieved by heating pumice to expand it still further.

Many countries have areas of pumice. In some cases the deposits are old and the surface layers have weathered into soils which are often used for agricultural or horticultural production. In other areas enormous volumes of young unmodified pumice deposits are available for exploitation. Iceland in particular is a major source of pumice for horticultural use in the Netherlands and other European centres, although Greece and its islands is also a substantial producer.

## Characteristics of pumice

Pumice destined for use as a granulate material in horticulture is graded, usually within the range 2 to 6mm diameter when it is intended for use as a substrate, although finer material is sometimes included in the mix. The particle size distribution in a batch of pumice is an important factor in determining the air to water ratio within the substrate. Finer grades of pumice, 0 to 2cm or 0 to 4cm, are also used for particular purposes. Fresh pumice is sterile, having had no contact with any source of weed seeds or plant pathogens at its origin.

Pumice is a stable material which can withstand sterilisation by steam without any substantial loss of structure. It can therefore be used for several successive years, resulting in a low annual cost to the grower.

It is relatively light material, with a typical bulk density of about 500kg/cu m. This is approximately five times as heavy as perlite.

An important requirement of any horticultural substrate is that it should be available in adequate quantities and that its quality should be consistent. Pumice meets this requirement in that material from any particular source will be acceptably consistent in its physical and chemical characteristics, and that it is available in substantial quantities at a reasonable cost.

## Air/water ratios

Horticultural quality pumice graded to 2 to 6cm has a pore volume of around 80 to 85%. Depending on the level of the water table this typically results in a water-holding capacity of 50 to 60% and an air content of 25 to 35%. These levels are very suitable for substrate growing as the root zone will have an adequate supply of both water and air at any stage of the irrigation cycle. Like perlite, It has very good vertical capillarity and this, combined with its high air content, makes it ideal for use in a basin system with a permanent reservoir of water at ground level. Finer grades hold proportionally more water, and therefore less air, and have to be managed accordingly.

By adjusting the range of granule sizes in a mix it is possible to produce different air to water ratios for specific purposes. One supplier offers three horticultural grades. The standard material, with a capacity of 45% water and 40% air, is suitable for the principal horticultural crops like tomatoes, cucumbers, roses and chrysanthemums. A finer grade, which will retain 60% water, and which therefore contains only 25% air immediately after irrigation, is intended for rooting cuttings. A coarse grade, holding only 30% water at capacity, is ideal for those crops which need a high air to water ratio. The three grades can also be characterised by their bulk density. The fine material weighs 600kg/cu m when dry, the standard grade weighs about 500kg, and the coarse grade only 450kg/cu m.

## Nutritional status

Pumice is chemically quite inert, but it does have a degree of cation exchange capacity (see chapter 10). When the material is new it contains no significant amounts of soluble nutrients other than a little potassium and sodium, and it therefore has a low electrical conductivity, around 0.1 to 0.2 mS/cm when measured in a water extract.

When it is first used it releases some sodium into the nutrient solution, and with some crops this may lead to unacceptable sodium levels for a short time, especially if there is also some sodium in the water supply. The release of sodium is accompanied by some retention of nutrients such as calcium, potassium and phosphate, but this is minor and once the exchange has stabilised there is no further retention of nutrients. These initial changes are accompanied by an increase in pH of about one unit from its starting value of around 6.0 to 7.0 as the system stabilises.

A recent introduction on to the substrates scene is a pumice growing slab. This has been developed in Iceland and was introduced as a commercial product in 1995 following successful trials the previous year. It remains to be seen how pumice slabs will perform under commercial conditions and whether it has any future as a serious competitor to the established slab materials.

## Fungicidal properties?

There are suggestions that pumice has some fungicidal or insecticidal properties. This has not at the time of writing been conclusively proven, but a trial in Italy comparing pumice and peat as soil additives demonstrated that carnation wilt was considerably suppressed by the mix containing pumice, but not by the peat mix. A similar observation was made in relation to root diseases of woody plant seedlings when they were grown in mixes containing either pumice or sand.

## GROWING TECHNIQUES

Pumice is most commonly used in the same way as perlite. The two materials have very similar physical characteristics (chapter 3).

Beds are arranged to have a 2 to 3cm undrained reservoir in the base to provide a continuous source of nutrient solution to the root zone, which is situated immediately above this height. The excellent capillarity of horticultural grade pumice makes this possible.

Pumice is usually irrigated several times a day, using a small volume each time, but experience with perlite has shown that this is probably not necessary, and twice daily or even daily waterings may prove to be adequate in most situations.

### Pumice and peat?

Pumice is sometimes used in combination with other media such as sand or peat, but there is no evidence that mixtures are any better than pumice alone. In Italy, for example, a tomato crop grown in a 1:1 mix of pumice and sphagnum peat was compared to one grown in pumice alone, with a substantial advantage emerging in favour of the all-pumice substrate.

Pumice is also used in many countries either as a soil additive or as a constituent of container mixes for a wide range of subjects, where it is used in combination with peat, soil, bark or other media.

### Containment systems

A number of different container systems have been used successfully for pumice, including individual polyethylene bags, longer multi-plant bags, plastic boxes, and polystyrene boxes. If the individual containers share a common drainage gully which can equalise differences in water distribution caused by variations in the irrigation system, then the crop receives overall a very uniform water supply.

For vegetable crops, a substrate volume of 6 to 12 litres/plant is commonly used, arranged in such a way as to give a substrate height of around 12 to 15 cm. Whichever system is used it is important to make sure that there is a consistent 2 to 3 cm reservoir of nutrient solution in the base but no restriction to drainage above this height. In this way all plants will receive an adequate balance of water and air in the root zone, and larger volumes of dilute feed can safely be applied whenever it is necessary to rebalance the nutrient solution.

As an alternative to the use of individual containers in a gully arrangement it is also possible to use pumice in an ebb-and-flow system, particularly if less depth of material is required by the crop. An ebb-and-flow pumice system has been successfully trialled in Holland for radish production. In this system the beds are free-draining at the base, but each irrigation cycle floods the beds to a depth of a few centimeters. This depth must be retained long enough for movement of the nutrient solution up through the substrate by capillarity before it is released.

The advantage of ebb-and-flow systems is that they make fuller use of the available depth of substrate for rooting, so a smaller volume of material can be used. The disadvantage is that irrigation management becomes a little more critical. There is also less hindrance to the spread of diseases through the crop than with a semi-isolated system.

In common with other granulate materials such as perlite, the nutrient solution which is held within the substrate cannot be effectively extracted directly for analysis. In a reservoir system it is possible to draw solution from the reservoir itself, but this does not give a reliable picture of of what is present in the root zone.

The most widely used technique is to sample the substrate itself from the volume which contains the roots, collecting a small amount from each of about 20 sites within the glasshouse. This volume is then thoroughly mixed and a sub-sample is shaken with distilled water in the ratio of 1 to 1.5 substrate to water. This extract is analysed and the results are reported as the level of each nutrient in the extract.

This means that the conductivity, for example, cannot be related directly to recommended conductivity levels in slab substrates, which are measured without dilution.

## PRACTICAL EXPERIENCE — AROUND THE WORLD

Pumice is becoming quite widely used as a substrate in Europe and in North America, which has its own sources of raw material.

*In the Netherlands*    So far the main crops grown commercially in pumice in the Netherlands are tomatoes, cucumbers, roses and chrysanthemums, although several others have been tried on a smaller scale. Research in Iceland, aimed at increasing worldwide awareness of pumice as a growing medium, has demonstrated that it can also be successfully used for the production of capsicums and gerberas on a commercial scale.

   Most recently Dutch research has been looking at pumice as a possible substrate for the production of amaryllis bulbs in closed growing systems in place of sand and expanded clay granules. In a preliminary trial at Naaldwijk experimental station two sources of fine grade pumice came out top of a range of alternative materials. Apart from the environment pressures which are demanding closed systems, growing amaryllis in an inert material like pumice is now essential for export of bulbs to many countries, including Japan and the USA, which will not allow the importation of any plant material which is 'contaminated' with an organic growing medium.

*In Jersey*    Pumice has become a popular substrate for carnation production in Jersey following extensive trials at the Howard Davis Farm experimental station. Continuous troughs were found to carry too great a risk of disease spread, so 3 to 5 litre plastic buckets are now used with four to six cuttings planted into each. The pumice is washed through before planting to adjust the substrate pH and to remove unwanted sodium and the finest particles. This also settles the pumice into the containers. The pots are placed on polystyrene slabs for insulation and to encourage free drainage. A drip irrigation system giving 1 to 2 litres/hour has proved suitable, but overhead or hand watering may also be necessary if a new crop is being established under stress conditions.

*In Greece*    Pumice is also popular in Crete, which has its own source of horticultural quality material. Strawberry production in vertical tubes has proved to be successful, using black polyethylene tubes 15 to16cm in diameter and up to 2m long, filled with either pure pumice or a mixture of pumice and peat or some other locally-available organic medium. In one comparative trial the mixtures proved to give better results, probably because nutrient and water distribution from top to bottom of the tube was more easily managed.

*In Japan*    The Japanese have their own substantial supplies of good quality pumic and, the material has been successfully demonstrated for many crops, and in particular for container-grown indoor trees, shrubs and ground cover plants.

*In Italy*    An attempt was made in Italy to add slow release fertilisers to pumice as an alternative to the continuous use of soluble NPK fertilisers in the nutrient solution. A tomato crop was used to compare the two options. Although both materials produced similar results in the trial, the use of slow-release fertilisers is not likely to provide a reliable alternative to the complexities of feeding a long-term crop in an inert substrate like pumice.

# 5 Polyurethane foam

*Production and characteristics of polyurethane foam. Growing techniques and systems.*
*Reusing polyurethane foam. Practical experience.*

Interest in polyurethane foam as a horticultural substrate began in Belgium. Like many substrates, including rockwool, the horticultural potential of polyurethane foam was first investigated as one way of utilising a material which was either already being produced on a large scale for industry or which was available in large quantities as a waste product from manufacturing. In the case of polyurethane foam the initial interest was generated by the availability of offcut waste from the furniture trade. The successful development of this source of foam has led more recently (in the UK at least) to the manufacture of low density polyurethane foam slabs specifically for horticultural use.

Although there are risks with the large-scale use of waste products as horticultural substrates, particularly in the uniformity of the material, they do have an environmental advantage in that they usually need relatively low energy input in their manufacture.

The first slabs based on polyurethane foam were made from chipped waste material, and these are still widely used as a horticultural substrate, particularly under the trade name Aggrofoam. For this material, foams of different densities and pore sizes are chipped down to a uniform size then mixed together in suitable proportions and compressed to form homogenous blocks of the desired density. The bonding process involves applying superheated steam at a temperature of 120C, so the end product is both sterile and stable.

## Characteristics of polyurethane foam

Polyurethane foam is structurally very stable, with a useful life span of up to 10 years. It can be effectively and economically steam sterilised between crops (p25).

The slabs are resistant to damage. Unlike rockwool a slab which is stood on will return to its original shape without any change in its characteristics. Re-used foam slabs have been compared with new slabs for the production of several crops with no detectable deterioration in crop yield or quality. Re-used slabs may actually perform rather better than new ones in some circumstances, probably because the presence of old roots in the structure may improve the water holding capacity of the substrate.

At first the reliability of polyurethane foam products was suspect because there were indications of toxic effects from the fire retardant materials which are added to foams used in the manufacture of furniture. This problem now appears to have been eliminated with the wider horticultural use of polyurethane foam slabs in Europe.

One significant characteristic of the bonded material is that it has a lower water holding capacity than most other substrates. In many situations this can be an advantage, but there have sometimes been problems with drying out when crops have been grown through intense summer heat in combination with low humidity levels inside the glasshouse.

The irrigation regime for polyurethane foam slabs has, therefore, to be different from that for a 'wetter' material like rockwool. Polyurethane foam slabs are very free-draining, and a stable air to water ratio is re-established within the slab very quickly after irrigation. This means that a crop in polyurethane foam has to cope with a relatively short period during which the water content is above optimum compared to a crop in a slower draining substrate like rockwool.

### Low density option

The most recent development in the use of polyurethane foam is a low density slab which is manufactured directly from homogenous virgin foam rather than from bonded foam chips. In the UK this product was launched as 'Richgrow'. This material is claimed to be easier to manage than the bonded foam because it has a rather higher water content at capacity, similar to that of rockwool.

Another advantage of non-bonded polyurethane foam slabs is that their physical characteristics are completely consistent from batch to batch, although this can probably also be claimed for bonded slabs now that they have become a major product in their own right.

A virgin polyurethane foam slab manufactured in the UK underwent two years of trials in comparison with bonded polyurethane foam slabs and rockwool for cucumber production. It was concluded that both new and recycled homogenous foam slabs performed at least as well as rockwool, and generally better than bonded foam slabs, and that they were particularly well suited to sterilisation and reuse. One notable observation was that far fewer roots were visible on the underside of the homogenous foam slabs at the end of the season than on either of the other substrates. Since the vigour of the crop was always good, this seems to indicate that the roots were better distributed through the volume of the slab.

### GROWING TECHNIQUES

Polyurethane foam slabs are very easy to re-wet after they have been fully dried out. Unlike rockwool even a completely dry slab shows no resistance to wetting. This can be very useful when the slabs are being prepared for a new crop after sterilisation. The water capacity of bonded polyurethane foam slabs is not high, however, and so it is important that enough water is applied before planting.

The total height of the slabs does not need to be as high as for rockwool because, especially with bonded foam, the best root conditions are found towards the bottom of the slab. A depth of 5 or 6.5cm is commonly used for this material, compared to 7.5 or 10cm for rockwool slabs. New homogeneous foam, despite having a higher water holding capacity than bonded foam, still has an adequate effective rooting volume for most crops in a 5cm deep slab, although some growers prefer to use a 6.5cm depth, especially if the glasshouse floor is not completely level.

### Planting up and feeding

The techniques for wetting up and planting into polyurethane foam slabs are much the same as those for rockwool. Even with the comparatively shallow depth of polyurethane foam slabs, it is better to slit the wrapping slightly above the bottom at planting time. This gives a temporarily higher water table within the slab and encourages roots to move from the propagation blocks into the slab. Once this process has begun the slit can be extended right to the base of the slab and the roots will continue to grow down into their final distribution pattern.

The nutrition of crops in polyurethane foam should follow the recommendations for rockwool, since both are chemically inert substrates. The irrigation regime for established crops on polyurethane foam does not have to be very different for a standard rockwool regime, but there is some evidence in the case of the drier bonded foams and in the early stages of crop establishment that more frequent waterings using a smaller volume each time will give the best results. Alternatively the frequency can be similar to that used for rockwool but a slightly larger volume applied each time to give a little more drainage overall. This option seems to work best for homogenous polyurethane foam slabs.

## Second cropping

The limited depth of polyurethane foam slabs can be a disadvantage when attempting to establish a second crop on the substrate in situ. The wrap is already slit to the bottom, so the water table within the slab, especially with bonded foam, will be too low to encourage rooting out of the propagation block into the growing slab.

One way round this problem is to place a small wedge of wood or plastic under the slab at the position of the drainage slit. This lifts the drainage point by a centimeter or so, and raises the water level in the slab enough to encourage the roots to grow down. Another way to achieve the same effect is to give very frequent small waterings during the first week or so after planting.

## REUSING POLYURETHANE FOAM SLABS

Polyurethane foam is a very stable material which, with adequate sterilisation between crops, can be reused several times. It is important to be able to do this, particularly with unbonded homogenous foam, because the material is relatively expensive and can only be justified economically if the cost can be spread over several seasons.

Foam slabs are easily and economically sterilised by steam. The dry foam itself is very light, and can be quickly brought up to 100C, at which temperature it is completely stable. It is necessary to remove as much of the water from the slabs as possible before they are steamed, because any residual water will add greatly to the cost of steaming without any increase in benefits. Irrigation should cease a week or so before the end of the crop so that the plants have time to take out a large proportion of the water left in the slabs. The aim should be to reduce the weight of a standard slab below about 1kg.

Fortunately the structure and handling characteristics of polyurethane foam makes the removal of any excessive residual water at the end of the season very simple. A roller press, such as a clothes mangle, set to a gap of about 1cm will squeeze out most of the remaining water. Alternatively the slabs can be unwrapped and placed lengthways along the heating pipes to air dry them. This may have the effect of distorting their shape, which can be a problem when the slabs are being stacked for steaming, but it has no long-term effect because they return to their original shape as soon as they are wetted. It is not necessary to stop short of drying the substrate out completely because, unlike rockwool, polyurethane foam will absorb water readily however dry it is.

Foam slabs are steam sterilised in the same way as rockwool. The slabs are stacked on wooden pallets, leaving a 5cm gap between adjacent slabs to aid the penetration of steam into the centre. A total height of about 1m, or 20 slabs, is generally used. Thermometer probes should be placed at suitable points within the stack to monitor the rise in temperature.

The stack is then completely covered with a steaming sheet, and steam is injected until the full volume has been at a temperature of 100C for at least 15 minutes. If pressurised steam is used, care should be taken that the temperature within the stack does not exceed 103C, above which the structure of the foam can be damaged. If the slabs are well dried before steaming the whole stack can reach 100C within about 15 minutes, although this can take an hour or more if the foam is too wet.

## PRACTICAL EXPERIENCE

Polyurethane foam slabs, both bonded chip and virgin foam, have been successfully used for many glasshouse crops. Initial experience with the substrate was derived mainly from Belgium and Holland, particularly on tomatoes and cucumbers. More recently polyurethane foam slabs have been used for other vegetable crops, including aubergines and peppers, as well as for all the major cut flower crops. Roses, carnations, gerberas, alstroemeria, bouvardia and anemones are all produced commercially in polyurethane foam slabs.

### Herbs on foam strips

One novel development is the production of leaf salads and herbs on thin foam strips. The technique, under development at the Sint Katelijne Waver research station since 1987, combines an NFT gully system with 2cm wide strips of recycled polyurethane foam. Expensive to set up, the system is most suited to crops like watercress and lambs lettuce which, with assimilation lighting through the winter, can yield up to 15 crops a year. One advantage is that the circulating solution can be cooled down to 15C in summer for heat-sensitive crops like chervil.

Work on the suitability of polyurethane foam slabs for cucumber production at HRI Stockbridge House in the UK involved new and used bonded foam slabs for two long-season crops compared with rockwool. It was shown that new foam slabs could produce the same yields as rockwool provided the irrigation programme was optimised for each substrate. The low water-holding capacity of the new bonded foam slabs meant that the standard rockwool watering regime did not always supply enough water to meet the demands of the crop.

Crops planted on to slabs which had grown one or more crops previously and which were steam sterilised before use, matched or exceeded the yields from either new foam or new rockwool. It was also reported that the polyurethane slabs suffered much less damage than rockwool slabs during the sterilising operation.

Polyurethane foam has also been tested in Germany and Ireland for cucumber production. In Germany it was compared with perlite, rockwool, a selection of organic growing media and expanded clay granules. In this case perlite came out best. The foam slabs also performed satisfactorily but water consumption was higher than for most of the other substrates, as was the drainage rate. These findings were only provisional however. Early results from Irish trials appear to show that the irrigation programme adopted favoured the wetter substrates like rockwool at the expense of relatively dry materials like polyurethane foam.

The lesson is not that polyurethane foam will not perform as well as some other substrates, but that it does need an irrigation regime appropriate to its water-holding characteristics.

### Granulate and flock forms

Most polyurethane foam is used in block or slab form, but it is also possible to obtain a granulate or flock produced from foam. This is manufactured from industry waste foam which is mixed and milled to form a medium suitable for use either as a compost additive or as a substrate in its own right. Polyurethane foam granulates have been successfully used for cut flower production as well as for hardy ornamental nursery stock production.

Tomato plants are commonly raised in rockwool cubes (above). In the glasshouse, they are sometimes stood on the polythene sleeve of the slabs for several days prior to being moved to their final position in the planting 'holes' (top)

[Pictures courtesy Grodania A/S & Rockwool Grodan BV]

Rockwool systems suit all types of tomato production, from cherry types to beef tomatoes like these (left)

Substrate techniques have fostered the glasshouse production of peppers in northern Europe and encouraged the crop's development, as in the introduction of fruit colours other than red or green; this orange fruiting crop growing in rockwool is typical.

Management of substrate-grown crops is demanding and the monitoring of factors like water content of slabs (below) is vital

[Pictures courtesy Grodania A/S & Rockwool Grodan BV]

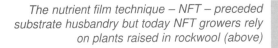

*The nutrient film technique – NFT – preceded substrate husbandry but today NFT growers rely on plants raised in rockwool (above)*

*Isolating the rockwool from the glasshouse floor with polystyrene slabs (right) helps keep the root system of crops like tomatoes warm*

Cucumbers are the classic rockwool crop. It was largely thanks to its up-take by Dutch cucumber growers that rockwool became the world's foremost inert growing medium

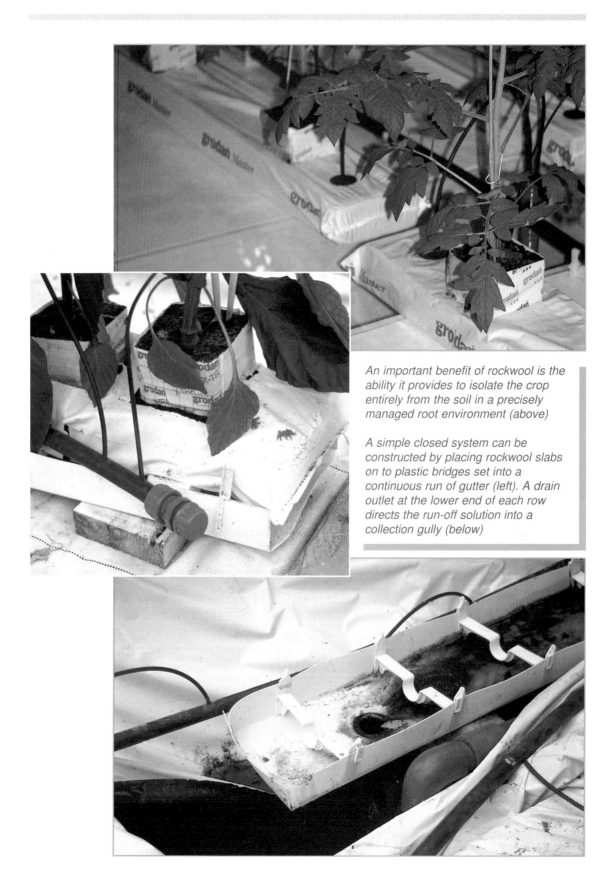

An important benefit of rockwool is the ability it provides to isolate the crop entirely from the soil in a precisely managed root environment (above)

A simple closed system can be constructed by placing rockwool slabs on to plastic bridges set into a continuous run of gutter (left). A drain outlet at the lower end of each row directs the run-off solution into a collection gully (below)

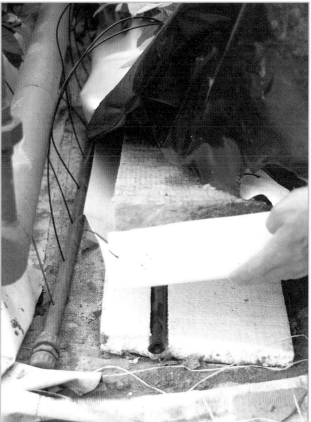

Systems of growing in rockwool can be set up reasonably cheaply. Channels can be constructed using flexible gullies like these (above) while a heating pipe embedded in polystyrene slabs under the gully is a simple means of providing root zone warming (left). Wrapped rockwool slabs can even be placed directly on to polystyrene (below). Here the supporting material is moulded in the form of a channel into which is set a perforated pipe to collect the run-off

Slabs of polystyrene can be inserted between the walls of the gully and the substrate to provide temperature insulation (left). Here two rows of rockwool slabs are set on to a double-width gully with central drainage channel (above). This channel is covered with a polystyrene slab to keep debris out of the recirculating solution

Used rockwool slabs ready for steam sterilisation. First old plant material is removed with care to avoid damaging the slabs, then the slabs are stacked on pallets leaving spaces between for the steam to circulate freely. Finally the stack is covered with a sheet to ensure all the material reaches sterilisation temperature quickly

*A healthy crop of aubergines growing in rockwool (left). The ability to manipulate the feeding programme according to the needs of the crop makes it possible to keep the plants in balance throughout the season, avoiding production flushes [Picture courtesy Dept of Horticulture, Howard Davis Farm, Jersey]*

*After tomatoes and cucumbers, peppers are the most important rockwool-grown food crop. In rockwool the crop's feed can be managed in such a way to maintain a good balance between vegetative growth and fruit develpment. Setting also remains free throughout the growing period (above). Various training systems have been used for peppers in rockwool but the single row V system is one of the most successful provided the irrigation system is accurate enough to cope with the small substrate volume*

# 6 Other substrates

*Glasswool. Expanded clay aggregates. Zeolites. Duroplast. Slagwool. Washed sand.*

This chapter deals with six materials which can and are used in crop production. In the mid 1990s they were all 'minor' products in terms of the cropped areas down to them. But each of them met a specific market demand and fulfilled a specific need.

## GLASSWOOL

Glasswool shares many of the physical characteristics of rockwool and it is generally used in much the same way.

The manufacturing process for glasswool is broadly similar to that for rockwool as well except that the raw material is quartz sand rather than basaltic rock. The sand is melted at 1,400C in combination with other ingredients including calcium carbonate and the molten mix is spun in large drums with perforated sides, through which the molten glass is forced by centrifugal pressure to form fibres. The fibre dimensions are established during this process, and they are then dried and bonded together in an oven before being formed into slabs of the required thickness and density.

At the time of writing the main source of glasswool in Europe was the French company Cultilene.

The manufacturing process for glasswool makes it possible to define the characteristics of the finished product accurately in terms of water and air holding capacity as well as density. The fibre orientation within a glasswool slab is claimed to give a better and more uniform spread of nutrient solution following irrigation than can be achieved with rockwool, particularly horizontally across the slab. This produces a wider irrigation cone and a better use of the slab volume for root establishment.

The average fibre size has a big effect on crop performance in glasswool. In one trial in Holland a cucumber crop produced a well distributed root system throughout the volume of glasswool slabs which had a fine fibre structure, while in coarser slabs the majority of the roots were at the bottom. It is likely that the higher capillarity in the fine structured slabs gave a better overall air to water ratio through the slab volume.

One advantage in particular which glasswool is claimed to have over rockwool is its structural stability. The bonding resins used to hold the fibres together in a rockwool slab are eventually damaged under acid conditions, so the structure of the slab gradually deteriorates. This does not happen with glasswool, which is therefore more resistant to low pH values, retaining its initial air and water distribution characteristics better through a long cropping period. It is also less likely to be damaged physically when it is moved at the end of a crop, so it is very suitable for sterilisation and reuse. Alternatively the used material can be ground, sieved and heated to 500C to yield a product which can be recycled.

## Variable structure option

Because the fibre structure and orientation of glasswool can be easily manipulated it is possible to form variable structure slabs which can take advantage of the different water distribution characteristics which can be achieved. One version of this is a slab which contains a gradient from top to bottom. The surface of these slabs consists of a very fine fibre structure, which allows applied feed to spread very efficiently across the slabs, producing a broad cone and thoroughly flushing out the slab solution. The fibres are progressively coarser further down the slab, with a particularly coarse and open structure at the base. This gives added structural stability and also ensures that the slabs drain very freely. The end result is a slab which, it is claimed, offers an exceptionally high useful volume in terms of root distribution.

Variable structure glasswool slabs have to be managed in an appropriate way in order to take full advantage of their characteristics. Obviously the first requirement is that they are placed on a flat surface the right way up, with the coarse fibres at the bottom! The wrapping should be cut to give a single drainage slit at the base of the slab in the middle of its lower side. Frequent small waterings – about 100 ml at each irrigation – should be used during the establishment period to get plenty of roots out of the propagation blocks and into the slabs as quickly as possible. Overwatering at this stage is unlikely, so at least 20% drainage should be allowed at every watering.

Early crops being established in glasswool when outside temperatures are low should be watered at least twice during the night to minimise the fluctuations in the slab solution conductivity which can be caused by high heating pipe temperatures and low humidity levels in the glasshouse.

During the summer it may be necessary to apply up to 50% drainage to a mature crop on hot sunny days to keep the slab conductivity down to an acceptable level. This is particularly important in the middle of the day and early in the afternoon, when the crop is taking up mainly water, otherwise slab conductivities can easily rise too high late in the day and through the night.

Variable structure glasswool slabs have a lot of active root close to the surface, so it is necessary to keep the top area of the slabs moist all the time. If the surface appears to start to dry out between waterings the best solution is to increase the frequency of irrigation and to reduce the volume applied on each occasion. Growers who have used rockwool and glasswool side by side have reported that glasswool needs on average one additional irrigation cycle a day. The generally lower water content of glasswool compared torockwool, perhaps of the order of 20%, is seen as an advantage for crops which prefer drier growing conditions, particularly gerberas.

## EXPANDED CLAY AGGREGATES

Expanded clay aggregates first found a use in horticulture as a growing medium for indoor ornamental plants and for roof garden cultivation. More recently there has been interest in using these materials for the glasshouse production of both flowers and vegetables. Much of the ground work on these materials has been carried out in Germany, where a wide range of expanded clays and expanded shales from a number of sources including Austria, Denmark and Belgium as well as Germany itself have been tested since the 1970's. The best known and longest established commercial product in Europe is the clay-based Leica.

Expanded clay aggregates and similar materials are produced by heating suitable clays or shales to a high enough temperature to fracture their structure and forming the resulting low density material into pellets. The individual pellets, which have an extensive pore structure, usually have a diameter of between 0.8 and 1.5cm. When the pellets are put into individual containers or troughs with a reservoir of nutrient solution in the base they have only enough capillarity to draw the solution up to a height of about 7 to 10cm, while leaving the top surface of the substrate relatively dry.

When they are first wetted up it can be difficult to establish adequate capillarity, especially if the particle size is large, and the substrate can easily dry out between waterings. While this can be a disadvantage for a lot of crops, it can be an advantage for some.

Unlike most of the substrates described in this book, expanded clay and shale aggregates have a substantial cation exchange capacity (see chapter 10). This means that when they are first irrigated with a nutrient solution they will absorb some of the applied nutrients – especially calcium, magnesium and potassium – and release others, including sodium. This may cause a temporary imbalance in the supply of nutrients to the crop until the capacity of the substrate is fully taken up, but once an equilibrium is established the crop will have access to whatever fertilisers are applied.

Some sources of the raw material for these substrates can be high in soluble salts, so it is necessary to test potential sources for salt content before they are used. If the sodium con-

## Roses in aggregate

Several rose crops in Holland and the UK have been grown in expanded clay aggregates for several years with very acceptable results. The aggregate has to be structurally sound, with few broken pellets or small material, otherwise it will not stand up to a long-term rose crop like roses.

It has been amply demonstrated that a good crop of roses can be produced on this substrate but that it is important to take account of its low water holding capacity and high porosity when establishing an irrigation regime. In a bucket system, for example, with two or three plants per container, it seems that at least 10 and up to 25 waterings of no more than 30ml per watering are needed, depending on time of year and the weather. In an open system the drainage volume has to be quite high, ranging from 40% in dull weather up to 60% or more during periods of maximum heat stress.

If it is not possible to set up a substrate heating system for a rose crop in buckets it is advisable to use irrigation water heating so that the large total volume of solution which is applied to the crop does not lower the temperature of the substrate and allow iron deficiency to develop.

tent of the substrate is high this will be exchanged for other nutrient ions and released into the solution. Even when a particular source of aggregate has been shown to be low in soluble salts there have been cases where unattributable crop damage has been reported, so it is possible that some sources contain contaminants which are not revealed in routine inorganic analysis.

Once the initial nutrient exchange problems have been overcome expanded clay aggregates seem to perform adequately in isolated growing systems. They do not have any obvious advantages over alternative materials, however, and their limited capillarity has prevented them from being widely adopted on a commercial scale. Where they are used they are generally either put into open trough systems with a small depth of reservoir in the base to maximise their capillarity or into large individual containers for specimen foliage plants, again with a reservoir in the base. The plants should be inserted well into the depth of the substrate to encourage rapid root development. Plants which are placed onto the surface of the substrate will not easily be able to root out into the dry top layer. (There is some interest in expanded clay aggregates in Holland for gerbera production because gerberas in rockwool are inclined to stay too wet in the winter.)

## ZEOLITES

Zeolites are granular rocks based on a crystalline aluminosilicate structure. There are various forms of zeolite with a range of physical and chemical properties, but they all have in common an open porous structure which allows them to take up and release water and exchangeable ions without any significant structural changes. Zeolites are major constituents of many volcanic rocks and they are mined in many locations, including the USA, Japan, China, Central America and Europe.

Unlike most of the substrates described in this book, zeolites are deliberately chosen for their high cation exchange capacity. This property is used to load the substrate with a suitable balance of nutrients before introducing the crop, with the result that irrigating with only water releases enough nutrients to sustain the crop for an extended period.

### Success in carnations

Much of the work on zeolites has been carried out in Jersey on standard carnations. A Bulgarian source of the zeolite clinoptilolite was chosen because it could be selectively loaded with ammonium nitrogen, phosphorus and potassium, and because the raw material is very low in sodium compared to some other types of zeolite. The zeolite was used in 5 litre plastic containers with four carnation cuttings put into each pot. A standard drip irrigation regime was used, except that no nutrient solution was applied at any time over the two years that the crop was grown. The water quality was good, but it did contain low levels of nutrients to supply the crop with those which were not provided in the zeolite.

The early results of this work have been encouraging. The first crop produced commercially acceptable yields of high quality blooms over an 18 month period with overall yields matching those from a standard crop grown in pumice. There was a significant reduction in nutrient leaching from the substrate compared to pumice but the nutrient uptake by the crop, as monitored by plant sap analysis, was normal.

The availability of nitrogen to the crop was relatively low, with the result that the drainage from the crop contained almost no nitrogen. Because of this the crop showed lower than usual sap nitrogen levels, but this was not reflected in production.

If nutrient-loaded zeolites can be shown to support other crops without any external source of nutrients then they may prove to be an interesting addition to the range of commercial horticultural substrates, particularly if environmental factors are taken into account. It is possible that a free-draining installation based on loaded zeolite could avoid the complications of recirculation but without contributing to environmental pollution from nitrates and phosphates.

## DUROPLAST

Duroplast foam is a brittle granular foam material which is more widely known for its use in flower arranging, for which it is marketed as Oasis foam. It has also found some success as a horticultural substrate, however, and duroplast foam growing bags are now used on a moderate scale for producing cucumbers, tomatoes and peppers in Holland. This foam has also proved to be a suitable substrate for plant propagation, and in the USA it is used in moulded plug form to root cuttings. Duroplast slabs between 4 cm and 6cm thick have also become available, with the higher water content of the thinner slabs being more suitable for vegetable crops and the drier thicker slabs being preferred for flower crops.

Duroplast foam has an open cellular structure. The basic material is inert, but additives with some cation exchange capacity can be incorporated into it to improve its performance when it is used as a rooting medium. It is claimed that duroplast foam can be used for several seasons without any deterioration in its physical characteristics, and that it can be handled while wet without breaking. It can be steam sterilised between crops without losing its structure.

Crops in duroplast foam growing slabs are managed in much the same way as those in rockwool, although their irrigation requirements may be a little different. Duroplast foam is exceptionally free draining, so frequent low volume waterings are needed. The slabs release surplus water very quickly, with 95% of the drainage volume appearing within five minutes after irrigation.

New Duroplast foam growing bags tend to have a rather low pH initially, and it is recommended that this is raised by watering the bags with a 0.1% solution of potassium bicarbonate before use to bring the pH up to about 5.5. This may not be necessary if the water supply has an adequate level of bicarbonate. The high air-to-water ratio in Duroplast foam makes it particularly suitable for flower crops which need a dry root environment, and it has been successfully used for orchids, alstroemeria, carnations, anemones and bouvardia.

Duroplast foam can also be used in granulate form mixed with between 30% and 60% rockwool granulate to produce a substrate with the desired air-to-water ratio for any particular crop.

## SLAGWOOL

A material described as slagwool is produced in Egypt as a by-product of the country's iron and steel industry. It is manufactured into a granulate form with a similar appearance to rockwool and with broadly similar physical characteristics. In American trials on tomatoes it was compared with rockwool and perlite in individual containers. The crop data from this trial showed a consistent yield advantage over both perlite and rockwool but more evidence will be needed before it is likely to be adopted on a large scale.

## SAND

Sand is being increasingly used as a commercial horticultural substrate, particularly in Holland where growers are obliged to move into closed systems on environmental grounds and where, especially with bulb and corm crops, they are looking for systems which can be managed in much the same way as soil and yet be isolated from the glasshouse floor.

Washed river sand in troughs meets this need, although the feeding regime for a crop in chemically inert sand is more demanding than for a soil-grown crop. It is important to find a source of river sand which has the desired physical characteristics for use as a substrate. For this reason Dutch growers have started to move away from German sands and towards sources in Iceland, despite the much greater cost. The best results have been obtained with sands which have a particle size range between 2 and 5mm. If the mix contains too much material finer than this the capillarity will be too high and it will be difficult to provide enough air to the roots. The risk of root pathogens like rhizoctonia spreading through the substrate will also be greater.

The sand is used in wide V-shaped troughs, preferably with a central drainage pipe to collect run-off solution and through which steam can be injected to sterilise the substrate. A slope along the trough of 0.1% is enough to provide adequate drainage, especially if there is a central pipe. A reservoir should not be used with sand because this will only aggravate the excessive capillarity of the material.

Sand is a good material for many bulb crops which are likely to be damaged at harvest. The roots are too easily pulled out of a lighter medium like rockwool granulate or peat, and freesias, gladioli and iris have all performed well in sand troughs. UK research has shown that year-round chrysanthemums also do well in sand, with up to eight successive crops being grown without any significant increase in root disease and without sterilisation between crops. Bouvardia has been successfully grown in a 15cm depth of washed river sand in large plastic boxes.

# Part 2 – Growing techniques

## 7 Crop production systems

*Open systems. Closed non-recirculating systems. Closed recirculating systems. Solution sterilisation. Pathogens in substrate systems.*

There are a number of ways in which substrates can be used to produce horticultural crops. Many of the more popular materials, such as rockwool, polyurethane foam and glasswool, are manufactured in slab form. These can either be used in an open system, set out in rows either on benches or directly on to the glasshouse floor, or in a closed system, in which they are contained in gutters or gullies or on a profiled floor with a drainage collection system.

Most other commercially used substrates, particularly lightweight granulates like perlite and pumice, are put into pots, bags or bolsters and used in much the same way as slab materials. These granulates, and heavier materials like sand, can also be used in a trough system, usually with a V profile and a central channel to contain and collect the drainage from the troughs.

When rockwool was first used it was thought of as an extension of nutrient film technique and it was managed in much the same way. NFT is based on a continuously recirculating solution so it was natural to set up a rockwool system in a similar manner. It soon became obvious, however, that recirculation in rockwool had few benefits and a lot of disadvantages.

With more experience, rockwool growers lost their initial enthusiasm for recirculation and turned to open growing systems. That is, the surplus solution which had to be applied to flush out the substrate was allowed to run directly to waste. This is the simplest and most manageable option for substrate growing, particularly if the quality of the water supply is not very high, because it disposes of unwanted salts so that they can be replaced with fresh nutrient solution. Any root diseases resident in the substrate are also less likely to spread through the crop, as each growing unit – slab or bag – is more or less isolated from the others.

Environmental pressures on growers changed the picture completely, particularly in countries like the Netherlands where horticulture is concentrated in large areas and the environmental effects of allowing nutrient solutions with their contained salts to run to waste are similarly concentrated. The requirement rapidly becoming the norm in countries like Holland is for total containment in a closed system, so that no nutrient solution enters the environment, either directly or through the glasshouse floor, other than in a controlled and environmentally acceptable way. This means that a closed system is the only option, whether it is based on slabs, bags or troughs.

There are two forms of closed system. In one the drainage is collected but it is not re-applied to the crop. An acceptable method of disposal still has to be found for the drainage as it is produced. In the other alternative the drainage, together with any unwanted salts or disease organisms which it may contain, is recirculated back to the crop. The advantage in this case is that nutrients and water are used more effectively, with a minimum of waste. The disadvantage is that the solution may need expensive treatment to remove unwanted salts or to eliminate diseases before they are spread through the crop. Even with full recirculation there will be occasions when some or all of the contained volume of nutrient solution has to be dumped, but at least this can be done in a properly managed way under controlled conditions.

### The options

In summary there are three basic systems for substrate management:

1       An open system, no collection or recirculation
2       A closed system, collection but no recirculation
3       A closed system, recirculation of solution to the crop

*Note: this is the accepted terminology in Europe. In the USA a system which collects the drainage solution but does not recirculate it to the crop is still referred to as an 'open' system.*

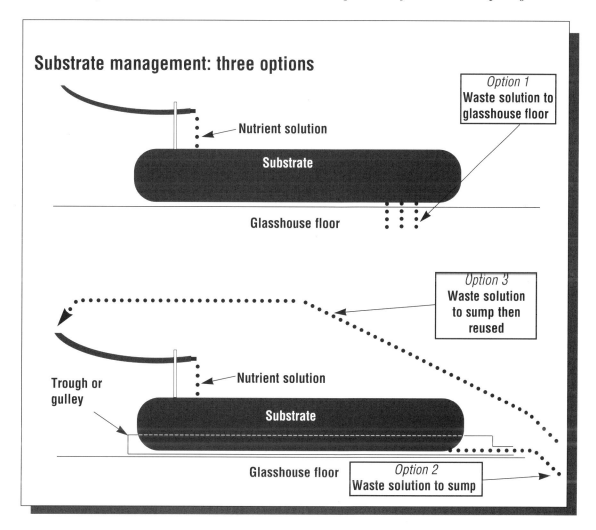

**Substrate management: three options**

*Option 1*
**Waste solution to glasshouse floor**

Nutrient solution

Substrate

Glasshouse floor

*Option 3*
**Waste solution to sump then reused**

Trough or gulley

Nutrient solution

Substrate

Glasshouse floor

*Option 2*
**Waste solution to sump**

## 1. OPEN SYSTEMS

This option is only available if there are no environmental pressures to minimise or prevent the release of nutrients, including nitrates and phosphates, or salts such as sodium and chloride into the ground water in the immediate vicinity of the nursery. In some parts of Europe this is already prohibited.

The simplest arrangement for using a substrate in an open system is to set individual slabs, bags or pots of the substrate directly on to the glasshouse floor, which is generally covered with poly-ethylene to isolate the system from soil-borne diseases and to prevent the crop from rooting out of the containers into the soil. One or more plants are put into each slab or container, and a drip irrigation system is set up to deliver nutrient solution directly into each unit. The slabs or containers are free to drain, usually from the base, and any surplus irrigation runs to waste through overlaps in the polyethylene sheet into the glasshouse soil.

Before the glasshouse floor is covered the surface must be graded. There can be a slight slope either along the length of the glasshouse or across the width of each row to make sure that the drainage runs away from each container and is not left in puddles to be drawn back into the containers between waterings. The gradient does not need to be more than about 1 in 50, and larger slopes are likely to result in the loss of some of the useful volume of the substrate. The best arrangement for most systems is to have the slope across the row, directing the drainage away from the working path. Overlapping the polyethylene floor covering between the double rows ensures that the drainage can escape and that the floor of the glasshouse will remain dry. This can be further helped by contouring a shallow gully between the double row to hold the drainage until it has time to soak through the overlap.

Apart from the drainage slope, the floor of the glasshouse must be accurately levelled. This is often done under laser control. It is particularly important that there should be no bumps or hollows along the crop row if slabs or polyethylene bags are used. If the floor is not level some units will fail to drain adequately and there is a risk of waterlogging or drying out of individual plants. One way round this is to place the containers on to polystyrene slabs, usually about 3 to 5cm thick. These are more or less rigid, so they discourage sagging quite effectively. They also have the advantage that they provide good thermal insulation, keeping the substrate temperature up to that of the glasshouse air rather than the floor, which is often a lot colder. For crops which benefit from high root zone temperatures a pipe loop can be set into a groove in the top surface of the polystyrene slabs to warm the substrate from below.

## 2. CLOSED NON-RECIRCULATING SYSTEMS

The first stage of containment beyond the traditional open system is to collect drainage from the substrate and to direct it to a storage sump or tank, from which it can be taken for disposal in an environmentally acceptable way. It is sometimes possible to use the drainage solution from a substrate crop to irrigate a nearby soil-grown crop or even to apply it to adjacent agricultural land. There are a number of layouts which allow for the collection of surplus nutrient solution, some of which are appropriate only for particular substrates.

Rockwool, glasswool or polyurethane foam slabs are usually put into a rigid channel system, of which there are several types on the market. The basic form of these is a simple channel running the length of the row into which the slabs are placed. These are relatively inexpensive and adaptable, but they have the disadvantage that drainage from individual slabs can be poor. A more serious problem is that the drainage solution can come into contact with other slabs further down the channels. The disease risks of this simple system are generally considered to be unacceptably high, so many growers now use a modified system which allows for the slabs to be raised above the base of the channel.

This is done either by sitting the rockwool directly on polystyrene slabs which are slightly narrower than the channel and which run the length of the channel, or by using a series of bridges of polystyrene or plastic spaced at intervals of 20 to 30cm down the row. Both of these options allow free drainage of the surplus nutrient solution away from the slabs and so get around the problem of disease being carried between adjacent slabs in the drainage solution. The bridge system is more expensive, but it is also more effective, providing the best root environment. The lower ends of the channels can be open, feeding the drainage into a collection gully or channel, which in turn carries it into a sump or reservoir. Alternatively the channels can lead directly into the collection system via closed pipes.

### Separated drainage

The most popular closed system for slabs and other substrate containers in Holland is separated drainage. This is a relatively inexpensive system which has evolved from the traditional open system layout. A narrow channel is dug out of the glasshouse floor between each double row. This channel is then lined with polyethylene. A drainage pipe is laid in the channel, which is covered over with the floor polyethylene. This is slit at intervals to allow the drainage to enter the collection channel, from where it is taken to a suitable sump or reservoir. If the glasshouse floor is properly profiled this system keeps the drainage away from the substrate and ensures good root conditions and hygiene. It cannot be used in a stony soil, because the channel cannot be graded accurately enough.

The main requirements of a closed non-recirculating system of this type are that it holds the slabs level, that it retains and collects all the drainage, and that it does not allow the waste nutrient solution to re-enter other slabs. All the other characteristics of proprietary systems are optional, and their value has to be set against the quite substantial costs of installing some of the more complex systems. The useful life of rigid systems is an important factor in cost comparisons, because a system that will operate reliably for 10 years or more can more easily justify high installation costs than a less permanent alternative.

## 3. CLOSED RECIRCULATING SYSTEMS

If a closed system is necessary on environmental grounds then it makes sense to consider the possibility of reusing the collected drainage. If the substantial volume of waste nutrient solution from a substrate crop has to be dumped, which is itself no simple task, then potentially valuable water and nutrients are being lost. The waste nutrient solution which is collected from a substrate system will usually contain a good level of all the nutrient requirements of the crop, often in more or less the right proportions.

The only justification for not recirculating the drainage back to the crop is that it may also contain unwanted elements. For example it is likely to contain excessive amounts of sodium, chloride and sulphate because these are present in most water sources or applied as fertilisers. They are not taken up in large amounts by the crop so they tend to accumulate. The worse the quality of the water supply, the more surplus nutrient solution has to be applied to the crop to prevent salt accumulation, so the more drainage is produced and the higher is the level of salts in the drainage.

To reuse drainage water effectively it is necessary either to install equipment to remove excess salts, which is possible but expensive, or to accept a progressive deterioration in the salt content of the circulating solution until it becomes unusable and then to dump all or a part of the total volume contained in the system.

Most growers use the latter approach, using the cleanest source of water to which they have access in order to minimise the frequency and volume of dumping. Some growers opt for the more costly alternative of removing both salts and nutrients from the drainage water before reintroducing it into the system.

## Disease risk

The other unwanted constituent of drainage from substrates is root disease. However clean the crop a few individual plants will occasionally suffer some root damage and disease will become established. One of the biggest advantages of substrate growing is that individual plants or small groups of plants are effectively isolated from the rest of the crop so root diseases cannot spread as quickly as they can in soil or an open growing medium. This advantage is lost if drainage containing root diseases is directed back into the bulk of the nutrient solution supplying the whole crop. Many root diseases can be very effectively spread from plant to plant in solution.

Despite the fact that many growers have attempted recirculation quite successfully without any means of preventing disease spread, it is becoming accepted that the only safe approach is to install sterilisation equipment to treat the drainage water before it is fed back into the system. A recent survey in Holland showed that about half of the growers using substrates, mainly rockwool, in a recirculation system sterilised their drainage solution.

The fundamental requirements of a closed recirculating system are therefore a means of removing excess salts, either by dumping or by treatment, and a way of sterilising the solution to remove disease organisms. Once these mechanisms are in place it is simply a question of arranging the plumbing to direct the treated drainage back into the system, either via the raw water storage system or as a separate operation.

The techniques for salt removal from drainage water are the same as those available for treating poor quality raw water (see chapter 8). Drainage solution sterilisation is considered below.

## Crop performance

Dutch tomato growers have been concerned about crop performance in recirculating systems in the last few years, often reporting weak growth, dark hard foliage and brown roots. A survey of the situation found that the reuse of drainage solution was not in itself the problem, but that the growers who had the biggest problems were those who did not sterilise either the solution or the substrate and who relied on the minimum volume of substrate per plant so that the root zone was always wet.

A trial on rockwool tomatoes was carried out in Holland in 1994 to demonstrate the safety of recirculation. In the absence of any particular problems with pathogens the performance of the crop, measured both as early and total yield, was almost identical for systems with or without recirculation, and with or without sterilisation of the drainage solution.

## SOLUTION STERILISATION

There are four established options for the sterilisation of drainage solution or raw water supplies on a commercial scale. They are heat sterilisation, ozone treatment, ultra-violet (UV) light treatment and hydrogen peroxide treatment. The first three offer complete sterilisation. Traditional hydrogen peroxide treatment may be more limited in its effectiveness, although there is a new treatment system based on this material currently being introduced commercially and which may give better results. Of the Dutch growers who have so far installed sterilisation equipment, 60% use heat, 30% ozone treatment and 10% UV treatment.

All of the main alternatives are expensive. According to a Dutch survey, if heat can be provided relatively economically from the glasshouse heating system then the first option is a little cheaper than the others, which all cost about the same per cubic metre of water or nutrient solution treated.

Despite the high cost of treatment, it is recommended in Holland to make use of the equipment once it is installed to sterilise not only the drainage solution but also the raw water supply. This is because it has been shown that raw water supplies in intensive horticulture areas often contain enough fusarium and other fungal pathogens to put crops at risk. So far few growers are prepared to go to these lengths but the situation could change if the problem worsens.

Heat treatment has been criticised because the end product is warm water

## A fifth option

An alternative method of sterilising drainage solution, sand filtration, is relatively inexpensive, but it appears to be fully effective only against phytophthora and perhaps to a lesser extent against pythium. It is therefore not safe to use as the sole source of protection for crops susceptible to root pathogens other than phytophthora.

If a sand filter is installed for this purpose it should consist of about one metre depth of sand graded between 0.2 and 2.0mm. The capacity of the filter should be related to the crop requirements if all of the recirculating water is to be treated. A sand filter system with a surface area of one square metre will treat approximately 5cu m of water a day.

with no oxygen content. However the water which emerges from an efficient heat sterilisation unit is only about 5C warmer. Once it is mixed with untreated raw water and piped back to the crop the residual heat is minimal. Oxygenation is in any case not a problem in substrate growing as it is in NFT, because most of the oxygen needed by the roots is provided by the air content of the substrate. In practice there is no evidence that drainage solution sterilisation by heating produces less satisfactory results than alternative sterilisation methods.

The new treatment based on hydrogen peroxide for water or nutrient solution treatment is marketed in Holland as Reciclean. It takes the form of two solutions which are introduced into the water from separate containers. One is a source of hydrogen peroxide and the other is an organic acid activator. When the two solutions are combined and introduced into the system at a strength of 100 ppm of hydrogen peroxide the treatment is claimed to deal effectively with fungal pathogens including both pythium and fusarium species. It takes eight hours before the treatment becomes effective, after which it remains stable and active for up to five days, although it is broken down when it comes into contact with rockwool. It is claimed not to be a hazard to horticultural crops.

## PATHOGENS IN SUBSTRATE SYSTEMS

Although substrate systems have the advantage that they can be isolated from most sources of root-borne pests and diseases, they have the disadvantage that any pathogen which does get into the system has easy access to its host, ideal conditions for rapid multiplication and the opportunity to spread rapidly through a large area.

A few viruses and a couple of bacterial pathogens have been found in substrate systems, but most of the diseases which are commonly encountered are fungal. These can be divided into two groups. The non-zoosporic fungi, including colletotrichum, thielaviopsis and verticillium, are relatively unimportant because they cannot spread effectively through the system via the nutrient solution. The other group – zoosporic fungi – is much more of a problem. This group, which includes species of phytophthora, pythium, olpidium and plasmopara, are able to move from plant to plant in the nutrient solution, and they can move very quickly through a closed system with devastating results.

## Sources of infection

It is obviously important to keep fungal pathogens out of the system from the start. Initial infection will often occur from contamination of the substrate with soil, but there are other possible sources. Pythium, for example, can sometimes be found in washed river sand – as a substrate or for glasshouse paths. It has also been found in ground water and reservoirs, although deep well water appears to be free from fungal pathogens.

If peat is used for propagating a substrate-grown crop it can be a significant source of pathogens, as can the planting material itself.

Once in the system pathogens can spread through the nutrient solution, even passing through sand filters. Many fungal diseases can also move directly between the roots of adjacent plants. Fungus gnats and other small insects have been shown to provide a means of fungal spread within the crop, too.

# Two-edged sword?

Sterilisation of the recirculating nutrient solution may occasionally be a two-edged sword. While it will eradicate most pathogens there may be circumstances in which it removes organisms which have a protective effect.

One possible example of this is in relation to the pathogen of rockwool tomatoes, Humicola. This is a saprophytic fungus which normally has no adverse effects on the crop, but it has been found that when tomatoes are grown in sterilised recirculating solution it can become much more aggressive, turning into a serious root rot pathogen. It is thought that this change may be caused by removing a secondary controlling organism in the sterilisation process, although a lot more work has still to be done before the mechanism is fully understood.

## Disease control techniques

Techniques for limiting the effects of disease pathogens in substrate crops include biological control with antagonistic organisms, treatment of the nutrient solution, and, usually as a last resort, treatment with chemical fungicides. A resistant cultivar is a possibility if a suitable one is available, but at present this is seldom an option. There are fusarium resistant tomatoes, and lettuce cultivars which are resistant to Plasmopara lactucae-radicis, but little else.

Biological control using antagonistic microorganisms is still being developed and the early results seem promising. However at the time of writing the only organism licensed for use on a commercial crop is Streptomyces griseoviridis, which is most effective against some species of fusarium.

Treatment of the nutrient solution (p42) can destroy circulating pathogens. Manipulation of the temperature of the substrate solution to take it outside the optimum range for pathogen development is another possibility, but one that has only limited application. For example Plasmopara lactucae-radicis will multiply only if the temperature is 25C or above, so running a low temperature regime will help control this problem, although usually at some cost in terms of crop performance.

The use of fungicides can at best be thought of only as a last resort. Most fungicides applied to most substrate-grown crops at a sufficient concentration to work effectively will also have an adverse effect on the crop. In most countries there are few if any materials registered for use on substrate-grown crops, so even if a suitable material can be found its use is likely to be prohibited, especially for an edible crop.

Non-fungicidal chemical treatments may be another possibility in the future, but more work needs to be done before their effectiveness and safety can be guaranteed. Potassium silicate applied to the nutrient solution, for example, may increase the resistance of the root system of particular crops to some pathogens. Another material with similar properties, chitosan, is also being investigated, as are a range surfactants or wetting agents, which may be able to prevent the spread of zoosporic fungi in recirculating rockwool systems.

# 8 Water supplies

*Water quality. Water storage. Water treatment. Acidification and pH buffering.*

An adequate supply of good quality water is essential for crop production in any isolated growing system based on a soilless growing medium. Even for open systems, water quality is a major factor in successful substrate growing. For recirculating systems, which will soon be the standard in most horticultural areas, high quality water is vital.

The most important aspect of water quality is its dissolved salt content. This is measured by its electrical conductivity. The more salts that are dissolved in the water, the more easily it can conduct electricity. So a high electrical conductivity indicates poor quality.

Some of the ions which contribute to the total salt content of water are useful nutrients. Most ground water sources contain some calcium and magnesium, and often smaller amounts of nitrate and potassium. As long as the levels are lower than the requirement for the crop they are not a problem. The feed formulation can simply be adjusted to take the contribution of each nutrient from the water into account. They can even be considered a benefit in that they reduce the total cost of fertilisers.

## Electrical conductivity

The electrical conductivity of water or a nutrient solution is a measure of its total dissolved salt content. The more salts in the solution, the more easily it conducts electricity. The conductivity of a solution can be referred to in either of two ways: *Electrical conductivity (EC)* or *conductivity factor (cf)*.

These terms are interchangeable and are measured in the same units. The ability of the solution to conduct electricity is measured by passing an electrical current through it with a piece of equipment called a conductivity meter. This gives a figure for electrical conductivity, which is usually meaured in milli-Siemens per centimeter, abbreviated to mS/cm. Micro-Siemens per centimeter (µS/cm) is sometimes used and 1mS = 1,000µS, so a conductivity of 1.5mS/cm is the same as one of 1,500µS/cm. Conductivity changes with temperature, so the measurement should also refer to the temperature at which it is made, usually either 20C or 25C.

Less useful ions like sodium, chloride and sulphate which are present in the water supply are bigger problems than dissolved nutrient ions. They are not required in significant amounts by the crop so they tend to accumulate in the substrate, especially in a recirculation system. They add to the total conductivity of the nutrient solution.

This is a disadvantage for three reasons. Firstly, they can generate within the substrate a conductivity high enough to reduce the growth rate of the crop. Secondly, they can make it difficult to formulate a balanced feed, leaving only a small margin between the conductivity resulting from the salt content of the water and the desired conductivity of the nutrient solution. Thirdly, they can interfere with the up-take of nutrient ions such as potassium and calcium.

By far the most suitable water supply for substrates is rainwater. Freshly collected, this will contain no significant amount of salts and so it will have a very low conductivity. It is always easier to add what is needed to a water supply than to remove what is not wanted. Rainwater does not contain any 'free' nutrients such as calcium, nor does it have any pH buffering capacity (see p50), but these minor disadvantages are negligible compared to the flexibility which rainwater offers in the formulation of nutrient solutions. Rainwater collected from the roof of the glasshouse can sometimes contain high levels of zinc from galvanised gullies.

Some water sources are almost pure rainwater, but many contain significant amounts of unwanted salts, especially sodium and chloride. Both of these are major constituents of seawater which in many horticultural areas is the original source of the contamination.

There is no absolute figure for the salt content of the water supply above which substrate growing is not a viable option. The level of sodium and chloride which will build up in the substrate depends on a number of factors, such as the percentage over-watering to drainage (see panel) in an open system, or the frequency of solution replacement in a closed, recirculation system. As a broad guideline, a water supply with more than 30 to 40 ppm of sodium will make the management of a recirculating system difficult for most crops, while a sodium content above 60 to 70 ppm will usually produce problems even in an open system.

If water of this sort of quality is all that is available then there are two practical courses of action. Either use any available rainwater to blend with the water source to improve the average water quality, or treat the water supply to reduce its salt content down to an acceptable level.

## WATER STORAGE

If available sources of water are of lower quality than is suitable for substrate growing, then the possibility of collecting and using rainwater should be investigated. Even if it is not practicable to collect enough rainwater to supply all of the crop's needs, a blend of rainwater and other sources will often be enough to bring the average water quality within range. Rainwater can often be considered on economic grounds whatever the quality of other water sources, provided it can be collected and stored in sufficient quantities at a reasonable cost.

The availability of rainwater will obviously not match the day to day needs of the crop, so this leads to the question of water storage. The theoretical volume of rainwater which could be collected from a glasshouse site if none ran to waste is easily calculated. A millimeter of rainfall is one litre per square metre; an inch of rainfall is 4.5 UK gallons per square yard. So a site which has 500mm (20in) of rain a year will receive 5,000cu m of water on a one hectare site (440,000 gal/acre) in the course of the year.

If all of the rainwater could be collected from a one hectare site and used as it was needed then an average rainfall of this amount would be able to meet the total demand of about half a hectare of cropped area, allowing 25% extra for drainage. So the rainwater collection area would still need to be twice the glasshouse area in order to meet all the needs of the crop even if it were possible to provide adequate storage. In practice this is seldom realistic. To store even enough rainwater for one month's demand for one hectare of glass in the summer would need a storage capacity of at least 1,500cu m, or a reservoir 2m deep with a surface area of 750sq m.

Although the sole use of rainwater is not often practicable it is still worthwhile to consider a storage reservoir if space is available. In this way at least some of the potentially available rainwater can be collected and used on the crop, either to blend continuously with other water sources or to refresh the system at intervals. If a recirculation system is installed then some storage capacity will in any case be valuable to collect, adjust and blend the circulating nutrient solution with fresh water.

If the principal source of rainwater is the roof of the glasshouse there can be a problem with the quality of the water which is collected from the first rainfall after an extended dry period. During the dry spell the glasshouse roof and other collection surfaces can become contaminated with pollutants such as pesticides and residues from heating boilers. There can also be significant quantities of zinc in the water if the glasshouse is constructed from galvanised steel. Usually, however, the levels of these pollutants would not be enough to cause any problem in the crop because the volume of water collected would be diluted into a much greater volume.

A bigger problem in an intensive horticultural area like the Westland of Holland is that the first flush after rainfall can carry pollutants into the environment if the glasshouse storage capacity is already full. Legislation now exists to prohibit growers from releasing 'first flush' rainwater, which is defined as the first 5cu m collected from each hectare of glass each time it rains. A number of alternative installations have been designed to enable growers to conform to this requirement.

# Crop water up-take

The table shows approximately how much water is taken up by a full-cover crop in northern Europe. No allowance is made for over-watering to provide drainage, so in many cases the actual irrigation volume averaged over the year will be about 25% higher. The figures were calculated from the water up-take of tomato crops grown under southern UK light conditions, but they can be broadly applied to most actively-growing healthy crops once they reach maturity.

Water consumption estimates are calculated from average light levels recorded outside the glasshouse according to the formula: 1 megajoule/square metre = 2,200 litres/hectare

The data can be adjusted to take into account the actual light levels which are recorded in a particular growing area to give a more accurate pattern for that area.

| Month | Daily average light* | Daily consumption litres/ha (gal/acre) | |
|---|---|---|---|
| January | 2.6 | 5,720 | (500) |
| February | 5.0 | 11,000 | (965) |
| March | 9.2 | 20,240 | (1,775) |
| April | 14.4 | 31,680 | (2,780) |
| May | 18.1 | 39,820 | (3,490) |
| June | 20.1 | 44,220 | (3,880) |
| July | 19.6 | 43,120 | (3,780) |
| August | 16.2 | 35,640 | (3,125) |
| September | 11.4 | 25,080 | (2,200) |
| October | 6.4 | 14,080 | (1,235) |
| November | 3.1 | 6,820 | (600) |
| December | 2.0 | 4,400 | (385) |
| **Year average** | 10.7 | 23,500 | (2,060) |
| **Annual total** | 3,900 | 8,600cu m | 750,000gal |

* MJ/sq m

## WATER TREATMENT

Water treatment in this context means the removal of unwanted salts. It is quite distinct from the water treatment techniques used to clean and sterilise nutrient solutions, as described in chapter 7. There are four basic techniques for removing salts from raw water, of which only one – reverse osmosis – has so far been found to be generally suitable for horticultural purposes on the grounds of size, capacity and running costs.

Reverse osmosis works by passing the water under pressure through a membrane which allows pure water to pass through but restricts the passage of the dissolved salts. The end product is an improved quality water on the downstream side of the membrane and a more concentrated salt solution upstream, which then has to be dumped. The system is widely used by many of the larger growers in Holland. It is effective, but the need to find an environmentally sound way of disposing of the concentrated salt solution which is generated can be a problem.

One alternative treatment system occasionally used is deionisation, in which the water is passed through two resins to remove the unwanted salts and replace them with harmless hydrogen and hydroxyl ions. These then combine to form more water. The resins have to be regenerated at regular intervals by flushing out the salts with strong acids and alkalis, producing another disposal problem.

Distillation and electrodialysis are two other options, both needing relatively high energy inputs to do the job.

In every case, however, there is an ultimate need to find a way of disposing of the salts which have been removed from the water.

All of these systems will give good quality water, equivalent to rainwater and much better than is needed for successful substrate growing. They can all handle poor or very poor quality water without difficulty. Distillation, for example, is often used to convert seawater into drinking water.

All of the options are expensive however. Reverse osmosis is costly to install but relatively cheap to operate, while some of the alternatives are cheaper to install but have much higher running costs. Horticultural reverse osmosis equipment can cost as much as £50,000/ha to install. A typical installation will produce up to 40cu m of water a day at a salt removal rate of about 90%.

## ACIDIFICATION AND pH BUFFERING

The acidity of the nutrient solution in contact with the plant's root system must be within a limited range if crop nutrition is to be satisfactory. If the solution is too alkaline then the plants will not be able to take up some of the nutrients adequately. Other nutrients, notably phosphorus, will form insoluble salts in the substrate and these will cease to be available to the crop until the pH is reduced to the normal range.

Similar problems occur if the nutrient solution is too acid, and in this case there is the added danger than the substrate itself may be damaged.

## INTERPRETING pH MEASUREMENTS

The unit of measure of nutrient solution acidity or alkalinity is pH. A pH of 7 is described as 'neutral' because it is in the middle of the range of pH values which run from 1 to 14.

The optimum pH value for the nutrient solution in contact with a root system in a substrate is between 5.0 and 6.0 for most horticultural crops. Since most substrates (other than new materials for the first few waterings) have little influence over pH, the input nutrient solution should also be within the same range. The pH of the raw water source is not a useful measurement, because of the lack of buffering capacity in many waters (see below).

Plants have the ability to change the pH of the nutrient solution in the root zone quite dramatically. At some stages of growth they will cause the pH to drift upwards, and then as the crop moves into another growth stage the effect on pH can suddenly reverse. To stabilise the pH of the solution in the substrate against these changes the formulation of the feed solution is adjusted to provide what is known as buffering capacity. This principle is also to used to correct chemically-induced pH drift. Another option is to make use of the crop's ability to change the pH itself, and to provide more or less ammonium in the feed to stimulate this ability (see chapter 10).

## pH AND BUFFERING CAPACITY

The rate at which the pH of water or a nutrient solution can be changed by outside influence depends largely on its buffering capacity. This is a measure of the content of certain ions, particularly bicarbonate and carbonate ions. This is measured – and described – as bicarbonate alkalinity.

The more bicarbonate there is in a water or a nutrient solution, then the higher its pH will be, and the more resistant it will be to external factors lowering the pH. The aim should usually be to keep a bicarbonate buffer of between 50 and 100 ppm in the substrate solution, and to use a nutrient solution containing about 50 ppm of bicarbonate to maintain this level in the substrate.

Many water sources, particularly poorer quality ground waters, contain too much bicarbonate alkalinity, often as much as 200 or 300 ppm. This has to be reduced before use and this is achieved by the process of acidification. A suitable acid is put into the feed at a rate which is calculated to neutralise, and therefore remove, all but the last 50 ppm of bicarbonate. If the water source is very consistent this can be done by adding the right amount of acid into the stock nutrient solutions. It is generally safer, however, to use a pH controller to measure the acid requirement (indirectly, by monitoring the pH of the feed) and to inject the appropriate amount of acid into the dilute feed solution to leave just enough buffer. If the pH of the feed is adjusted to between 5.0 and 5.5 this will usually leave about 50 ppm of bicarbonate alkalinity in the solution.

When rainwater or another similarly pure water source is used the problem is reversed. There is little or no buffering capacity in the water so it has to be added. In this case a suitable source of buffer, such as potassium bicarbonate, is added to the fertiliser mix. This is acceptable when the water source is consistent but for a variable water source it is better to use a pH controller. This cannot be done directly, because the pH measurement of unbuffered solution is not reliable. It is more usual to firstly add rather more bicarbonate or other buffering material than is needed to the mix, then to use acid via a pH controller to remove the surplus back to the required level.

### Acids and alkalis

The most commonly used acids for pH adjustment are nitric acid and phosphoric acid because they provide nutrients (nitrate and phosphorus respectively) at the same time. It is also possible to use either hydrochloric acid or sulphuric acid provided they are of a suitable grade for horticulture and free from contaminants. If an increase in alkalinity is needed the most suitable material is potassium bicarbonate, although sodium bicarbonate is sometimes used. This has the disadvantage of adding more sodium to the solution – a particular problem with recirculation. Carbonates are less suitable, as are hydroxides, although both are sometimes used for this purpose.

Horticultural acids are generally quite concentrated, often between 60% and 90% or more. They can be added to stock mixes in this form, but for injection via a pH controller they should first be diluted by about 10 times for more accurate pH control.

If acidification is done by adding acid to the stock solutions, it is important to know what the bicarbonate alkalinity of the water source is, and if it is variable it should be regularly checked. This is best done by a horticultural laboratory, but if this is not practicable it is possible to monitor bicarbonate, both in the water and in the substrate solution, on site. The only expensive item needed to do this is a pH meter, which every substrate grower should have anyway. The only other requirements are two glass containers, one graduated in millilitres (to 100ml) and one ungraduated (to hold 500ml), and a supply of 0.01N hydrochloric acid.

A freshly collected sample is used to rinse the containers, then 100ml is measured out and transferred to the larger container. 100ml of the acid is then prepared, and added in stages to the water sample until the pH has fallen to 4.5. The pH drop will be slow at first, then more rapid, so smaller quantities of acid should be used in the later stages. Note how much acid has been used to get down to pH 4.5, and multiply this figure by 6.1 to give the bicarbonate alkalinity as ppm of bicarbonate. So a water sample which is acidified by using 23ml of 0.01N hydrochloric acid has an alkalinity of 140 ppm of bicarbonate.

## Calculating the acid requirement

The amount of 60% nitric acid which will reduce the bicarbonate content down to 50 ppm is calculated as follows:

> *One litre of nitric acid, put into 1,000 litres of stock solution and diluted at 1:100, neutralises 7 ppm of bicarbonate.*

If 80% phosphoric acid is used the calculation is:

> *One litre of phosphoric acid, put into 1,000 litres of stock and diluted at 1:100, neutralises 6 ppm of bicarbonate.*

In either case, if the acid is stronger or weaker the formula should be adjusted in proportion.

Leaving approximately 50 ppm of bicarbonate buffer in the solution after acidification gives a safety margin while still bringing the pH down to about 5.5 or a little above. It is not safe to aim for a residual buffer of less than about 25 ppm of bicarbonate, even if a lower pH would be an advantage. This is because below this level a very small increase in acid would result in a very large reduction in pH. If the dilution equipment is slightly inaccurate, the pH could be reduced to a dangerous level.

As the bicarbonate content is gradually removed by adding increasing amounts of acid, the pH changes very little at first. A reduction in the bicarbonate level from 200 ppm to 75 ppm lowers the pH by only 0.8 units. From then on, though, the effect of further addition of acid becomes more dramatic, until between 25 ppm bicarbonate and 0 ppm the pH falls by more than 2.5 units. A very small further addition of acid will then reduce the pH even lower.

It is possible to add the required amount of acid directly to the full volume of feed, either in the raw water storage tank or after nutrient dilution. This is not usually recommended, however, because it is very difficult to get an adequately uniform mix throughout such a large volume. Also, it can only be done if the volume is known and fixed, so it is not suitable for a water storage system which is topped up via a float switch or ball valve mechanism.

# 9 Irrigation

*Irrigation systems and control equipment. Light/water relationship. Irrigation management. Nozzle blockages.*

One of the most important requirements for successful substrate growing is an accurate and reliable irrigation system. With the exception of large open beds of granulate substrate such as pumice or sand, which can be irrigated quite effectively with low-level spraylines, substrates need a well-designed and well maintained drip irrigation system.

The characteristics of the system in terms of the number of nozzles per unit area and the design flow rate from each nozzle depend on the substrate and the crop. As a general rule, vegetable crops like tomatoes and cucumbers are usually supplied with *one drip nozzle per plant* with an output of between *1 and 5 litres per nozzle per hour*. Higher density crops like carnations may have a similar number of nozzles per unit area, but not necessarily one per plant.

## System design

The glasshouse area should be divided into a number of units, each capable of being independently irrigated and fed. The size of each unit will depend on the layout of the nursery and the cropping programme, but should not usually be more than 0.4ha, or one acre. The pumps, mains, filters and distribution lines should be laid out and maintained so that every nozzle operates at its design flow rate and therefore delivers the same volume of nutrient solution over the same period of time.

Areas of the glasshouse which are known to have a particularly high or low water requirement should be provided either with a different number of nozzles or with nozzles with a different flow rate. Increasing the number of nozzles is usually the safer option. Pressure regulators are sometimes used in pipework to reduce output in some areas of the glasshouse (eg on sloping sites).

Depending on the crop and the substrate, the optimum flow rate from each nozzle can be between 1 litre and 5 litres per hour, and commercial drip irrigation systems are available to provide outputs within this range. Modern large-bore drip systems are designed to minimise problems with blockages, and these should always be used in preference to the older lace-type systems, which are not reliable enough for use with substrates. The best nozzles are those which feed the nutrient solution directly into the substrate rather than dripping it from some height, because these are less likely to become blocked with chemical residues caused by evaporation from the tip of the nozzle.

## IRRIGATION CONTROL

It is not practicable to assess by eye when a substrate crop needs water and to switch on the irrigation system manually. Water has to be applied exactly in proportion to the volume which has been taken up by the crop since the last watering, and the information needed to make such a decision is too complex to be done reliably without mechanical assistance. For the same reason, setting the irrigation system to operate from a time clock is not usually satisfactory, although this can be acceptable if it is combined with a more accurate technique to make any adjustments to the applied volume which may be needed from time to time.

There are two basic techniques which are available for accurate irrigation control.

The first is to continually monitor the amount of light the crop is receiving, to convert this information into the volume of water which has been taken up by the crop since the last application, then to apply the same volume to replace it plus any extra allowance for drainage. This is known as light integration. It works well, because experience has shown that the amount of light reaching a crop is by far the most important factor in determining the amount of nutrient solution it uses.

The alternative technique is to measure how much solution has been taken up from the substrate and to use this measure to determine when and how much to apply to replace it. This is done either by monitoring the water table level in the substrate, known as the start tray principle, or by monitoring the weight reduction which occurs in the substrate as its water content decreases.

### Light monitoring

A light integrator measures the amount of light which falls on a sensor positioned inside or outside the glasshouse. It adds these measurements up to give a cumulative total of light received at that point over a period of time. If the sensor is positioned outside the glasshouse then the light measure is described as 'global', and to calculate the amount of light which passes through the glass

---

## Measuring light

Light can be measured either as an instantaneous reading – known as *light intensity* – or as the amount received over a period of time, the *light integral*. There are various units in which light can be expressed:

*Light intensity:*   Watts per square metre (W/sq m)
lux (lumens/sq m), kilolux (klux)
lumens per square foot (lum/sq ft)

*W/sq m and klux are not directly convertable, as one measures all wavelengths and the other measures only light in the photosynthetic range.*

1 W/sq m is approximately 0.11 klux
1 lumen/sq ft is approximately 10.7 lux

*Light integral:*   gram calories per square centimetre (gcals/sq cm)
Megajoules per square metre (MJ/sq m)

1 gcal/sq cm is approx 0.042 MJ/sq m.

*Most light meters used in horticulture are integrators, recording the amount of light received over a period of time. They are usually, but not always, calibrated in Megajoules/square metre.*

to reach the crop a correction factor is applied for loss of light transmission through the structure.

The system therefore monitors the amount of light reaching the crop, and triggers an irrigation cycle at appropriate intervals based on a set light integral. For example, a reading of 110 Joules may represent 500ml of water uptake per square metre, or 200ml/plant in the case of a tomato crop. Whenever the light integral reaches 110 Joules, a 250ml irrigation cycle is triggered, 200ml to replace the crop demand and 50ml for drainage.

## RELATIONSHIP BETWEEN LIGHT AND WATER UP-TAKE

The relationship between the light integral (see panel) and water up-take can only be approximate as there are a number of variables which can influence it. So a light integration control system cannot be set up and left to run unchecked for long periods. When it is first put into operation its effect on the water content of the substrate should be monitored closely for several days to make sure that the factor which has been built into the system is appropriate. If the crop is receiving too much or too little water then the factor must be corrected accordingly. Even when it has been fine tuned in this way it should still be regularly checked because factors like crop vigour, growth stage and fruit load will all have an effect on the relationship between light and water up-take.

One limitation of light integration is that it is not able to take into account any residual water requirement during the hours of darkness. Some crops demand, or at least benefit from, night irrigation for various reasons. Without it the substrate can dry back overnight or the substrate solution conductivity can rise to an unacceptable level. Long periods without irrigation can also lead to precipitation of insoluble fertilisers in the lines and therefore to nozzle blockages. To get around this problem, many light integration irrigation controllers incorporate a separate timed cycle facility which allow the grower to trigger one or more waterings, either at night or during the day.

### Start tray measurement

Direct measurement of water uptake by the crop either by using a start tray or by weighing a representative volume of the substrate avoids the problem of water uptake at night by continuously monitoring the uptake of water by the crop and triggering an irrigation cycle whenever the uptake has reached a set value. With either start trays or weight monitors it is preferable for separate sensors and control systems to be installed in each glasshouse or for each irrigation unit. This is because the variation in water uptake between different areas of the crop can be great enough to make accurate irrigation management of the whole nursery very difficult. Even with a limited area under the control of each sensor it can be difficult to find a position within the crop which is consistently representative of the whole area.

The start tray is a contained volume of substrate, usually two or more slabs or bags positioned in a representative area of the glasshouse. The level of the water table in the substrate is monitored, usually electrically, so that when it falls to a set level an irrigation cycle is triggered. This can either apply a standard volume of nutrient solution which replaces the volume taken up by the crop, plus extra for drainage, or it can continue to water the crop until the level in the tray reaches a second, higher mark. In this case it is known as a start/stop tray.

As with light integration it is necessary to monitor the performance of a start tray control system. If the volume of water being applied to the crop is too much or too little the probe which triggers the start of the irrigation cycle should be lowered or raised respectively until the system is operating correctly.

There are a number of commercial start trays and related devices. All of these work on the same underlying principle but they often incorporate one or more extra features which are claimed to make them more effective. With start trays it is important to keep an eye on the few plants which draw water from the sensor unit. If they are less healthy or active than the crop as a whole, or worse still if one of them is damaged or even dies, then the unit will no longer be representative of the whole crop. If this happens, the unit will need either to be re-calibrated or, if practicable, moved to a more suitable group of plants.

## Weight monitoring

The third option for irrigation control, monitoring the substrate weight, is less commonly used in commercial crops, although there are proprietary systems based on this principle. Weight controllers are only suitable for crops like tomatoes or cucumbers, where the weight of the crop is carried on the crop support strings, or for free-standing plants such as ornamentals. Netted crops like roses or carnations cannot be reliably monitored in this way.

One or more slabs or bags of substrate within a representative area of the crop are set on a tray which is supported on a weighing platform. This incorporates a relay switch to trigger an irrigation cycle whenever the total weight of substrate plus the contained nutrient solution falls to a set value. Weight monitoring for irrigation management is more popularly used for crops planted in individual units, such as for plant propagation or for the production of ornamental plants in individual containers.

There is still no way of continuously monitoring the water content within a substrate like rockwool or polyurethane foam. This would be a valuable addition to the range of glasshouse monitoring equipment because an on-line substrate moisture sensor would make it possible to supply nutrient solution to the crop much more precisely according to its needs. One way in which this may be achieved is being evaluated in Belgium. Known as a thermal conductivity sensor, the equipment measures how well heat moves through the substrate between a heat source and a detector. The wetter the substrate, the higher the thermal conductivity, so measuring the heat dissipation from the source gives an accurate measure of the moisture content of the substrate. This information can then be used by a computer to control the irrigation programme. The system has been successfully demonstrated on a tomato crop, but further work remains to be done before thermal conductivity sensors can be safely introduced commercially.

## IRRIGATION MANAGEMENT

The frequency of irrigation and the volume which should be applied on each occasion depend on the crop and the substrate it is growing in. In the majority of cases a mature crop will need several applications of nutrient solution every day, sometimes as many as 12 or more. These applications will not usually be spaced equally throughout each 24 hour period. In some instances all watering will be done during the day, while in others one or more waterings will be needed at night.

The volume of nutrient solution applied to the crop on each occasion can be as little as 50ml or as much as 500ml. In the former case the accuracy and reliability of the irrigation system is extremely important. In the latter, the ability of the system to apply a large volume quickly may be important, to make sure that the cycle has been completed for each area of the nursery before the next cycle is due to begin.

## Drainage volume

In most substrate systems, whether they are open or closed, recirculating or free-draining, it is necessary to apply more nutrient solution at each irrigation than is needed to replace the volume which has been take up by the crop. This surplus is known as drainage, whether or not it is allowed to drain from the total system. The percentage of drainage needed depends on a number of factors, of which the quality of the water source is one, but in most cases the average drainage volume will be between 10% and 40% of the volume applied to replace water uptake by the crop. The object of this drainage volume is to ensure that the level of each nutrient in the substrate solution does not differ by too great a margin from that in the input solution. In the early days of rockwool it was thought that 10 to 15% drainage was adequate in most situations, but with more experience it has become clear that most crops need an average drainage volume of 25% or more.

If there is no drainage volume the substrate solution will soon be quite different from the input solution. The crop will take up water and leave certain nutrients, such as calcium, behind to increase in concentration. It will deplete some nutrients in the substrate solution, notably potassium and ammonium nitrogen. Relatively unwanted ions such as sodium and chloride will build up rapidly in the substrate. The only way in which these changes could be avoided in a system which is completely undrained would be by supplying a nutrient solution whose constituents are always present in exactly the same proportions as in the solution take up by the crop, and this will never be possible.

If drainage is established then the imbalance between the input solution and the substrate solution will be minimised, and the greater the drainage percentage, the smaller will be the differences between the two solutions. Nutrients which are taken up by the crop at a high rate will still be reduced in the substrate solution but a proportion of this solution will be forced out to drainage with each watering, to be replaced by solution containing more of these nutrients. Other ions which are accumulating in the substrate will be flushed out and replaced by fresh solution containing less of them. Drainage therefore acts as a regulating mechanism to keep the differences between the substrate solution and the input solution to a minimum. The differences between the input solution and the substrate solution which are found by routine analysis are an important indication of whether the amount of drainage is inadequate or excessive.

In a closed recirculating system the effect of over-watering by a set percentage is similar, but in this case the final step has to be the removal from the system of the surplus volume of solution. If, for example, a recirculating system contains 20 litres of solution per plant, and the crop demand is 4 litres per plant per day, applying a drainage volume of 25% creates an increase in the system volume of 1 litre per plant per day, or 5% of its capacity. This volume therefore has to be removed from the system at frequent intervals to restore its working capacity. The effect on the nutrient balance of the circulating system is the same as for an open system with the same drainage percentage.

## Active drainage system

A novel approach to irrigation management which is being developed by Grodan specifically for rockwool crops is the active drainage system, or ADS. This was first considered in the late 1980s, but field testing is still in progress to refine the system before it becomes more widely available. Grodan's ADS system is geared to their own rockwool slab structure and its specific hydraulic characteristics.

The principle of ADS is that a suction head is established in each rockwool slab, and that this enables excess nutrient solution to be sucked out of the slab at the end of each irrigation cycle. The grower can therefore apply enough solution to more than saturate every slab in the glasshouse and then withdraw the surplus to leave an identical solution volume in every slab, irrespective of the imperfections of the irrigation system. The grower has complete control of the speed and volume of drainage. This approach has other advantages, for example, it allows more precise management of slab solution volume, and therefore conductivity, at night.

ADS is based on wrapped and unslit slabs. Drainage is switched from an open gravity system to a closed suction pressure system. Each slab is attached to the system through a high density plug of rockwool inserted into its upper surface, and it is through this plug that excess solution is drawn out after each watering. A vacuum pump is used to initiate drainage but the extent of the drainage, and therefore the volume of solution retained in each slab after drainage, is controlled by the level of the inlet to the tank into which the drained solution is fed. The collected drain solution can then be sterilised, supplemented and recirculated to the crop as with any other closed system.

One obvious benefit of ADS is that it converts an open system into a closed recirculation system without the capital investment in gutters and ducting which is otherwise needed. There is no outlet for drainage from the slabs other than through the suction plug, so nutrient solution cannot pass from the rockwool directly into the glasshouse floor. It also allows much greater uniformity of the air and water content of the slabs, irrespective of imperfections in the irrigation system. A further advantage is that the lack of drainage slits in the wrapped slabs ensures that the root system is totally contained within the rockwool.

More work remains to be done on the operation and management of Grodan's ADS, but there is no doubt that it, and other active systems which will undoubtedly follow in its wake, can contribute greatly to irrigation management of rockwool and other slab substrates.

## AVOIDING NOZZLE BLOCKAGES

Since one of the most important requirements for successful crop production in substrates is an accurate and consistent irrigation system, the potential for nozzle blocking has to be considered and all practical steps taken to avoid it happening. These steps include protecting the water supply against the build-up of algae, filtering the water to remove any bacterial or other contamination before fertilisers are added, controlling the solution pH and other factors which encourage chemical deposition, and filtering again to remove any deposits which have been produced in the system.

There are two main types of contamination which can cause nozzle blocking in drip irrigation, either separately or in combination. The first is biological contamination, which can include various types of algae and bacteria. These are invariably introduced from outside the irrigation system, usually as a contaminant of the water supply. The second is chemical contamination, which can be undissolved fertiliser residue from the stock tanks but is more commonly produced within the irrigation lines when conditions allow the formation of insoluble combinations of some of the nutrients present in the solution.

### Bacteria and algae

Most water supplies contain small amounts of bacteria and algae. If the water is drawn directly into the system these may have no opportunity to multiply sufficiently to become a problem. If the water is put into storage tanks or reservoirs, however, these organisms can develop rapidly, especially when the water temperature increases in the summer. The problem is greater when the water contains enough nutrients, particularly nitrogen and phosphorus, for the algae and other organisms to feed on. One solution to the problem which works well for tanks is to cover them with an antialgal cloth. This prevents light transmission to the water, greatly reducing the photosynthetic activity of any algae which are present, although it has little effect against bacteria.

There is no equivalent solution for open reservoirs, for which the second line of defence, filtration, is often the only realistic option.

At least one filter should be installed between the water source and the fertiliser injection point. Two may be needed if contamination is known to be problem. These should be of a suitable type and pore size to trap as much of the biological contamination as possible, and they should of course be cleaned and serviced regularly to maintain their effectiveness. Even with adequate filtration it should be assumed that there will be some algae and bacteria passing through into the feed. These will not be enough to cause blockages, but they provide a source of greater contamination if they are allowed to multiply within the irrigation lines.

## Fertiliser contaminants

The second source of contamination is from the fertilisers used to make up the nutrient solution. Horticultural grade fertilisers are not completely pure, although they are in most cases a lot better than the equivalent agricultural or industrial grades. Some of the major fertilisers will contain a small proportion of insoluble material, such as sand or resin used to coat the particles and improve their flowability. These materials will be left behind in the dissolving tanks, and the installation should be set up in such a way that they are not taken up into the irrigation lines. In some cases a second set of tanks, used only to pre-dissolve the fertilisers, can be worthwhile. If liquid fertilisers are available they are unlikely to contain any significant amount of insoluble material as they are effectively filtered during the production process.

A second set of filters should be installed downstream of the fertiliser injection point to trap any insoluble materials which have passed into the system. These ideally consist of one large filter directly after the injection point and a set of smaller filters, one on each irrigation harness before it divides into the individual header lines. Again these should be of a suitable pore size and cleaned on a regular basis to ensure that they function properly without reducing the pressure reaching the nozzles. Computer controlled systems often have downstream pressure sensors to trigger an alarm if the system pressure increases as a result of filter or nozzle blocking.

It is possible for the soluble fertilisers which make up the dilute nutrient solution to recombine to produce insoluble materials, particularly calcium phosphate and calcium sulphate. If the pH of the solution is below about 6.0 and if it the solution is not allowed to remain static in the irrigation lines for a long time then this is not a serious problem in practice. Even so, a fine white coating can often be identified on the inside surface of the irrigation lines indicating that this process is occurring.

A more serious situation can develop when residual levels of algae and bacteria in the irrigation lines are given the opportunity to multiply. When this bacterial contamination can remain in contact with the warm nutrient solution in the lines for an extended period, such as throughout the night, their activity can cause a dramatic rise in the pH of the solution, and this in turn can produce extensive precipitation of insoluble salts. The end result is severe nozzle blocking with a combination of biological and chemical contaminants. This risk is greatly minimised if one or more irrigation cycles, however small the applied volume, are triggered each night.

## Cleaning the system

There are various ways to clean the irrigation system, some involving flushing out either through the end caps or through the nozzles, either under pressure or with suction, or using alternating pulses of water and air to clear any blockages.

Chemical cleaning is generally used between crops, although it may be possible to use with the crop in situ if the layout is such that the chemicals can be flushed away without coming into contact with the substrate. The best material for chemical contaminants is acid, usually nitric acid. This should be diluted as necessary to give a final concentration at the nozzles of about 1.5%.

For bacterial contamination the preferred material is sodium hypochlorite (bleach), used at a strength of no more than 0.05%.

In either case the chemical should remain within the lines for 24 hours and then flushed clear. Concentrated acids should not be allowed to come into contact with the rockwool, even when there is no crop present, because they will destroy the structure of the material by breaking the resin bonding. If using both acid and bleach it is important to flush out the system *between* treatments with clean water. This is to avoid direct contact between the acid and bleach which could otherwise lead to the creation of toxic gases from the chemical reaction.

# 10 Nutrition

*Feeding crops in substrates. Monitoring and maintaining nutrient levels. pH and conductivity. Substrate analysis. Plant sap analysis. Cation exchange capacity.*

Most of the substrates included in this book are more or less chemically inert. An inert substrate is defined for this purpose as one that does not have any particular influence on the nutrition of a crop grown in it. Inert substrates do not react chemically with fertilisers which are added to them, so the nutrients in the substrate remain freely available to the roots of the crop. Neither do inert substrates provide a source of any nutrients for the crop other than those which are supplied in the nutrient solution.

This categorisation of substrates is by no means absolute. Some of the materials used as crop substrates, of which expanded clay granules is a good example, are certainly not chemically inert. They have an important characteristic known as cation exchange capacity (CEC), which enables them to hold on to particular nutrient ions and make them less available to the crop. Substrates which have a significant cation exchange capacity have different nutritional requirements to those of a genuinely inert substrate like rockwool. The bulk of this chapter describes the nutrition of substrates which are for practical purposes chemically inert. Materials which have a sufficient cation exchange capacity to affect the nutritional requirements of crops grown in them are discussed separately at the end of the chapter.

Unlike soil and other organic growing media, inert substrates cannot provide any nutrients for the crop nor can they affect the availability of any nutrients which are applied to them. Every nutrient which is required by the plants must therefore be added by the grower, including minor and often unconsidered micronutrients like molybdenum. This means that a complete nutrient solution must be available at all times within the root zone. In practice it also means that it must be supplied with every irrigation. 'Watering' an inert substrate means supplying a dilute fertiliser solution to it – clear water is never used.

## Nutritional balance

Keeping the right nutrient levels around the roots all the time is not easy to achieve. There is an optimum nutrient solution for each crop, and sometimes for each stage of growth of a crop. Both the total nutrient content, measured as the solution conductivity, and the ratios between all of the individual nutrients in the solution have to be monitored and regulated throughout the life of the crop. The limits of tolerance are quite low, so it is necessary to keep the level of each nutrient in the substrate close to its optimum value all the time.

Unfortunately the nutrient status of the substrate is not static. The levels of nutrients in the solution applied to the substrate will quickly be changed by the activity of the crop. Some nutrients will be taken up rapidly by the plants, depleting their level in the substrate. Other nutrients will be unwanted and will be left behind to accumulate in the substrate. Depending on the pH of the solution some fertilisers can be rendered insoluble and precipitate out in the substrate, in which form they will not be available to the crop. A reverse in pH can then convert fertilisers which had previously been locked up in this way back into their soluble form, making them once again available to the plants.

Nutritional balance is easier to regulate in an open growing system than in a closed system. In an open system each irrigation cycle causes a proportion of the solution which is held within the substrate to run to waste, to be replaced by fresh solution. If the amount of drainage is adequate this has the effect of keeping the balance of nutrients within target. In a closed system the added solution has to compete with whatever imbalance has already been produced, and it is only by dumping a substantial proportion of the volume held within the system that target values can be recovered.

## MAINTAINING NUTRIENT STATUS

Plants are able to adjust to less than optimum levels of most nutrients by increasing the performance of their uptake mechanism so that they can continue to take up adequate amounts. However they need time to make this adjustment (in some cases two or three weeks rather than a couple of days) so they cannot successfully cope with a sudden reduction in nutrient supply. For example a crop which is continually supplied with potassium at a half of its optimum level may show no ill effects at all. Suddenly changing the potassium level from optimum to half rate overnight, though, would probably result in severe potassium deficiency symptoms.

Conversely plants can become acclimatised to high levels of nutrients. An excessive nitrogen supply will cause the crop's nitrogen uptake mechanism to be partially switched off so that the plant is not overloaded, and little or no harm will be done. If the nitrogen level is then suddenly reduced back to normal the inhibition of nitrogen uptake cannot be reversed quickly enough and nitrogen deficiency will follow.

In both cases the way to avoid problems is clear, and it leads to the most important rule in substrate nutrition. *A consistent nutrient supply to the roots is much more important than a precise nutrient supply.* Sudden changes, even those

## Types of solution

There are four types of nutrient solution

*Input solution*
The dilute fertiliser solution which is watered on to the substrate or added directly to a closed system

*Substrate solution*
The solution which is in contact with the roots within the substrate. Also called the 'slab solution' in the case of rockwool and similar materials

*Drain solution*
The solution which runs to waste in an open system or which is removed at intervals from a closed system. Sometimes referred to as the 'leachate'

*Stock solution*
A concentrated fertiliser solution which is diluted, usually by a factor of between 100 and 200 to 1, to produce the input solution

which are designed to bring the nutrient status closer to the recognised optimum for the crop, will do more harm than good.

If the level of a particular nutrient in the substrate is too high or too low the input solution must be corrected slowly, preferably over a period of at least two or three weeks, and even longer in extreme cases.

The ratios between many of the individual nutrients in the substrate solution are also important. For example the balance between calcium and potassium is one factor which determines the ability of the crop to take up calcium and which, therefore, influences the development of calcium deficiency symptoms of one sort or another. This balance between the individual elements in a nutrient solution should not be underestimated.

The optimum level of a specific nutrient may be important, but its relationship with other nutrients will be more likely to determine whether the performance of the crop is limited by its nutrition.

## Ground rules
● Keep the nutrient status of the substrate solution as close as possible to the optimum for the crop and its stage of growth
● If the level of an individual nutrient in the substrate has been too low or too high for some time, do not try to correct it too quickly
● Monitor the ratios between the individual nutrients as well as their absolute levels. Do not increase or decrease a single nutrient at the expense of its balance with other nutrients

## MONITORING NUTRIENT STATUS

The nutrient status of a crop growing in a substrate can be monitored in various ways:

1. The input solution can be monitored to indicate that the right nutrient balance is being supplied to the system. This is not particularly useful, except to demonstrate that the intended fertiliser mix has been correctly prepared and diluted.
2. The substrate, or the nutrient solution within the substrate, can be monitored to show what nutrients are actually available to the crop any any particular time.
3. The drainage solution released from the system can be monitored to see what imbalances are developing.
4. The crop itself can be monitored to see what nutrients it has been able to extract from the system.

### Substrate analysis

Substrate analysis is the basis for nutritional monitoring. Unlike input solution analysis, measuring the nutrient content within the substrate is able to show which nutrients are being accumulated or depleted either by chemical activity or by plant uptake. This is essential if corrective action is to be taken to recover the optimum balance of nutrients in the root zone.

There are various techniques for substrate nutrient analysis which depend on the substrate and on the way it is being used. For slab crops like rockwool and glasswool it is usual to extract nutrient solution from the region of the slab which contains the bulk of the root system, using a large syringe. Alternatively, in an open system the drain solution can be collected. For granular substrates like pumice or perlite it is possible either to extract samples of the nutrient solution from the basin, or to collect a representative volume of the substrate itself and extract it either by centrifuging or shaking. Blocks or cubes of substrates can usually be sampled just be squeezing some of the solution out into a container.

Whichever method of sampling is used, chemical analysis is then carried out on the sample to measure the levels of all the dissolved nutrients present, but not normally those which have precipitated in an insoluble form. The results of this analysis are then compared to target levels and ranges to see what if any corrective action is needed to the feeding programme.

The accurate interpretation of substrate samples depends on the sampling method. Different results will be obtained by sampling a rockwool slab with a syringe compared to taking a drain solution sample. In the same way the results obtained from a substrate extract of perlite will have to be interpreted in a different way from those from a basin solution sample.

## MONITORING PROGRAMMES

One of the most important advantages of substrate growing is that the grower has the opportunity of maintaining an optimum nutritional status in the root zone throughout the life of the crop, making a major contribution to maximising yields and crop quality. This can only be realised if the nutrient status of the substrate is checked frequently and compared to target values, so that any required changes in the feeding programme can be made without delay.

There are three levels at which monitoring should be carried out if various sorts of potential problem are to be identified in time to avoid loss of crop performance:

1.  **Daily** measurement of the pH and conductivity of the input solution and of the substrate solution

2.  **Weekly** or two-weekly chemical analysis of the major nutrients in the solution in the substrate, preferably within the root zone

3.  **Monthly** chemical analysis of the micronutrients within the substrate

Every grower who is using an inert substrate should possess and use a portable conductivity meter and a pH meter to measure every day the overall status of both of these factors within the substrate. Sampling should be done at enough points within the crop to be sure that the results are representative of the crop as a whole, and the results obtained should be recorded and compared to look not only for sudden changes but also for more subtle trends which could give problems later on. Daily samples should ideally be collected at the same time each day, preferably early in the morning, to minimise climatic differences from day to day.

Daily readings should be tabulated or plotted graphically so that long-term trends can be identified at a glance. It is not enough to get the input solution right and to assume that the substrate solution must therefore be right too. The ability of the crop itself to modify both the conductivity and the pH of the solution in the root zone is nearly always greatly underestimated and if these factors are not monitored closely the effect on crop performance can be dramatic.

Many larger installations will have a computer controlled nutrition regime which includes continuous monitoring of the input feed to make sure that it matches the set target levels for pH and conductivity. If this is not available the grower should make frequent use of portable equipment to make sure that the pH and conductivity control system is operating correctly. In any case, computer monitoring cannot provide a complete and reliable picture of what is happening within the substrate throughout the glasshouse, so substrate monitoring by hand remains essential.

# Calibrating pH and conductivity meters

Portable pH and cf (conductivity) meters are an essential part of day to day nutritional monitoring so it is essential that the results which they generate can be relied on. Even laboratory meters will change their calibration characteristics over a period of time so it is certain that portable meters which have to suffer the much more rigorous environment of the glasshouse will need frequent recalibration if their output is to be believed.

## pH meters

Most pH meters are designed to be calibrated at two points – usually at pH 4 and pH 7 – although if a higher range is more important they can often be calibrated at pH 7 and pH 10. If accurate standard solutions of the two calibration points are set into the meter and both give the correct reading, then it is safe to assume that any sample which reads between these two points is also correct. Even beyond the calibration range the meter should retain sufficient accuracy for horticultural purposes.

pH meters should be calibrated frequently if their readings are to have any value, preferably each time they are used. By far the most common reason for errors is weak batteries and the batteries should be replaced regularly, especially if the meter does not have a battery performance indicator. If in doubt put new batteries into the meter before attempting to calibrate it.

To calibrate a meter at two points it is necessary to have two standard solutions which are known to be correct. These buffer solutions, as they are known, are quite stable but it is obviously important that there should be no cross-contamination between the two solutions otherwise their pH values will change. Depending on the manufacturer's instructions, one buffer solution is tested, and the meter adjusted to give the correct reading. It is usual to test the pH 7 solution first. The second buffer solution is then tested, and a second adjustment is made using what is often called the 'slope' control to get the correct reading for this buffer. If any major adjustment has been needed then it will be necessary to re-check both buffers again.

pH measurements are quite sensitive to variations in temperature, and most portable ph meters incorporate automatic temperature compensation. This takes some time to produce a stable and reliable reading, so some patience is required for accurate results. A few meters are not equipped with automatic temperature compensation, and with these it is only possible to get accurate and reproducible readings if the buffer solutions and the samples are brought to the same temperature before calibrating the meter and recording any sample values.

## Conductivity meters

Portable conductivity meters are calibrated in a similar way to pH meters, except that in this case it is usual to check the meter against only one calibration standard. This is enough to demonstrate the overall performance of the electronics, although it does not guarantee that readings which are far removed from the calibration value will be completely accurate.

To minimise this problem it is best to select a calibration solution which has a conductivity close to the normal range of readings expected. For example calibrating at 2.0 or 2.5mS/cm is suitable for most nutrient solution monitoring. A higher calibration point, say around 4.0mS/cm, may be more appropriate for some slab solution testing, particularly in the case of crops which are often grown at a relatively high conductivity, such as tomatoes.

Most conductivity meters are temperature compensated and they calculate a standard conductivity reading at either 20C or 25C whatever the actual temperature of the solution. This is important, because conductivity values change quite considerably with temperature. The references to conductivity in this book assume a reference temperature of 25C. If automatic temperature compensation is not available the samples should be read after being brought to a temperature as close to 25C as possible.

Samples should also be collected for laboratory analysis at weekly or two-weekly intervals, using an appropriate technique for the substrate and the way it is being used. A sample should be taken from each area of the crop where different results could be expected, such as areas with different ages of crop or different varieties or different feeding regimes. It is usually enough to analyse for the micronutrients every other time since changes at this level are less likely to occur quickly. It is often useful to take an input solution sample for analysis at the same time, but in most situations this is not so important.

If plant sap analysis or another form of plant tissue analysis is being used to monitor crop nutrition in more depth samples for this purpose should be collected at the same time.

## INTERPRETING SUBSTRATE ANALYSIS

The levels of nutrients in the substrate will not usually be the same as the levels supplied in the feed. This is because some nutrients are more readily taken up by the crop than others so these tend to be present in the substrate solution in lower concentrations than they are supplied. This effect is exaggerated if the rate at which nutrient is supplied in the feed is not adequate for the needs of the crop. It is also exaggerated if the irrigation rate is not adequate because there is less opportunity for drainage to correct any developing imbalance.

The nutrients which, under normal conditions, tend to accumulate in the substrate because they are less readily taken up by most crops include calcium, sulphate and iron. Those which are taken up more readily include phosphorus, potassium and manganese. It can therefore be expected that the former group will be present at a higher concentration in the slab than in the feed, perhaps around 125%, with a normal range of 100 to 150%. The latter group are more likely to be depleted by the crop, typically with about 75% left in the substrate, and a normal range of 75 to 100%.

### Irrigation rate

These levels can be used as a good guide to the adequacy of the irrigation rate. They are less easily interpreted in a recirculating system, where imbalances have a longer time to develop and do not necessarily reflect the current status of the irrigation rate.

Other nutrients can show an even greater difference between the input solution and the substrate solution; a full list is given in the table. These figures were obtained with tomatoes, but the data for most other crops are similar.

Sodium and chloride also tend to accumulate in the substrate, particularly chloride, very little of which is taken up by the crop. Ammonium-nitrogen, on the other hand, is taken up very enthusiastically, and only very small amounts are normally found in the substrate solution. The speed of up-take of ammonium is important in the use of ammonium in the feed to control the substrate pH.

## Input/slab differentials

| Nutrient | Slab target/input | Normal range |
|----------|-------------------|--------------|
| Mg | 200% | 100-300% |
| B | 150% | 100-200% |
| Ca | 125% | 100-150% |
| $SO_4$-S | 125% | 100-150% |
| Fe | 125% | 100-150% |
| Cu | 125% | 100-150% |
| Zn | 125% | 100-150% |
| $NO_3$-N | 100% | 75-100% |
| P | 75% | 50-100% |
| K | 75% | 50-100% |
| Mn | 75% | 50-100% |

## pH EFFECTS AND CONTROL

The pH of the substrate solution as a whole, and in particular that part of the solution which is in immediate contact with the roots of the crop, is vital to the successful nutrition of the crop. Balanced uptake of each of the nutrients is only possible if the root zone pH is within the range 5.0 to 6.0. Higher pH levels inhibit the uptake of several nutrients, particularly iron. They also cause some nutrients to become unavailable.

Phosphorus is a good example of this effect, being precipitated as insoluble phosphate at high pH, and becoming available again if the pH subsequently falls. Low pH produces less dramatic effects, but does change the balance of uptake of some of the micronutrients.

The primary control of substrate pH is by the use of an input solution with an adequate but not excessive bicarbonate buffering capacity, as described in chapter 8. This is not always enough to keep the substrate pH within acceptable limits, though, because the crop itself has the ability to change the solution pH around its roots quite considerably under particular growing conditions.

### Ammonium nitrogen

Fortunately there is a second line of defence against wandering pH values. This is the use of ammonium nitrogen in the nutrient solution.

Ammonium is taken up preferentially to any other source of nitrogen by most crops, and when it enters the root it is replaced in the solution by hydrogen ions. These are the raw material of acidification, so the more ammonium is taken up, the lower the substrate solution pH will fall. This is why nutrient solution recommendations for substrate crops often specify that a small proportion of the nitrogen should be in the form of ammonium. A typical figure is 7 ppm $NH_4$-N, enough to resist any upward move in substrate pH, but not enough to create excessive acidity.

If the crop shows a tendency to increasing pH, as identified in the daily monitoring programme, the $NH_4$-N content of the feed can be increased to compensate. This should be done in small steps, because the effect takes some time to show and there is a risk of over-shooting if growing conditions suddenly change.

A typical programme is to increase the $NH_4$-N in the feed in 7 ppm steps at weekly intervals, with a ceiling at about 35 ppm. This approach should be used only after the input solution pH and bicarbonate levels have been checked and, if necessary, adjusted.

If the substrate pH shows a strong tendency to fall this can be corrected either by reducing the ammonium content of the feed or by increasing the bicarbonate buffering capacity of the feed (see chapter 8). Reducing or removing the ammonium source is often enough. If the water source contains little or no buffering capacity then it will probably be necessary to avoid the use of ammonium altogether. This can be difficult, because ammonium is a significant constituent of most sources of horticultural grade calcium nitrate. In this case the only option may be to avoid calcium nitrate completely and to use calcium chloride instead.

## PLANT SAP ANALYSIS

Plant sap analysis is an effective monitoring technique for the nutritional status of a growing crop. Developed in Sweden and Guernsey, and now becoming increasingly popular in other horticultural centres, plant sap analysis is ideal for crops in substrates, where nutrient problems can develop more rapidly than in soil-based growing media. It has been successfully used both to develop and refine feeding programmes for various crops in substrates, as well as a routine monitoring tool for commercial crops.

The basic objective is to look into the plant to measure what levels of nutrients are present at any particular time. Traditional plant tissue analysis, apart from being too time consuming and expen-

*Right: Plants for a long-season pepper crop, raised in a rockwool block, growing in zeolite substrate in a trial at the Howard Davis Farm, Jersey. In this trial a recirculation system was used. Because the substrate is not nutrient-loaded, continuous feeding is needed throughout the season*

*Below: These standard carnation cuttings are planted in zeolite in 5 litre polypropylene pots in a Howard Davis trial. In this case the zeolite is nutrient-loaded and the crop relies on this loading for its nutritional needs and is irrigation with clear water only*

*[Pictures courtesy Dept of Horticulture, Howard Davis Farm, Jersey]*

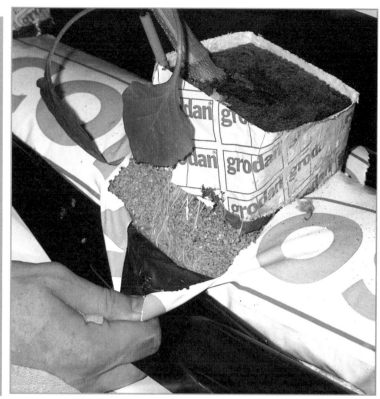

Standard carnation cuttings planted in 5 litre cyclinders of polyurethane foam (right). Chips of the foam in various grades can be bonded into cubes or slabs but the low-density version (below) is made from 'virgin' foam and has a higher water holding capacity than bonded material

[Pictures courtesy Dept of Horticulture, Howard Davis Farm, Jersey]

Opposite: Horticultural grade pumice is shipped in bulk from deposits like these in Iceland. In a trial at Howard Davis Farm, Jersey, standard carnations have been grown in pumice in 5 litre tubs (inset)

[Pictures courtesy Dept of Horticulture, Howard Davis Farm, Jersey]

Roses growing in expanded clay aggregate in buckets, each of which is irrigated by means of a mini-spray nozzle. In this young crop, the weak inital growth has been bent down to provide increased leaf area for photosynthesis

[Picture courtesy Ballakinnish Nurseries Ltd, Isle of Man]

Protected strawberry crops are becoming more common. This crop of Elsanta (left) was planted as cold-stored, bare-root runners straight into the rockwool slabs. The ones shown just planted out (below) are also Elsanta but were raised in a rockwool tray and planted into pre-drilled holes in the slabs

[Pictures courtesy Grodania A/S & Rockwool Grodan BV]

Melons growing in rookwool clabc undor plastic proctection in Spain. The growth of melons in rockwool is quite different to other crops – see p102

[Picture courtesy Grodania A/S & Rockwool Grodan BV]

Recirculating nutrient solution can be sterilised in a number of ways, one of the most efficient being heat sterlisation (above). One alternative is UV light (left) in which the solution passes in a transparaent pipe through a bank of fluorescent tubes. Another alternative is the biofilter (below). In this the solution is passed through a depth of sand (or other material) on the surface of which are activated bacteria which destroy any pathogens in the solution. A high temperature is needed therefore the system is usually housed within the glasshouse

*[Picture courtesy Ballakinnish Nurseries Ltd, Isle of Man]*

Every opportunity should be taken to collect and use rainwater for nutrient solution. Water from the glasshouse roof area can be piped to an adjacent reservoir (below) or tank. Where water (or recirculating nutrient solution) is stored in tanks outside, covering them with a light-resistant anti-algal screen (right) will avoid contamination with algae and bacteria

[Main picture courtesy Ballakinnish Nurseries Ltd, Isle of Man]

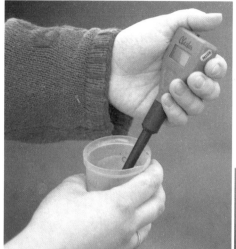

A regular pH check on the water supply (left) will indicate any build-up of algae in the storage tank

Filters should be incorporated in the irrigation system to keep drip nozzles clean – one right after the fertiliser injection point like the one shown below (the light blue assembly) is particularly important to trap undissolved fertilisers. Invidiual in-line filters (bottom) should also protect each irrigation harness

Picture (above) courtesy Ballakinnish Nurseries Ltd, Isle of Man

sive, is not well suited to this task. Nutrients which have been incorporated into the structure of the plant over a period of weeks or months are extracted and included in the analysis. What is needed is a measure of only those nutrients which are in soluble form within the plant sap, and which can be assumed to have been taken up by the plant over a much shorter time scale. This is exactly what plant sap analysis provides.

# Cation exchange capacity

Not all of the substrates included in this book are chemically inert. Some have a significant effect on the nutrients which are added to them, holding on to some ions and releasing others. This ability, which is seen to its fullest extent in humus-rich clay soils, is known as cation exchange capacity, or CEC.

The CEC is usually measured as milliequivalents (meq) per 100g of substrate, with many clays having a CEC value in the range 25 to 75meq/100g. This can go up to 150meq or above if the clay has a high humus content. Even a material like perlite, which is for all practical purposes considered to be chemically inert, has a CEC of up to 5meq, while vermiculite is about as active as sphagnum peat at around 100 to 150meq.

The cation exchange capacity is a measure of the sum of the exchangeable cations which the substrate is able to adsorb on to its surface. The substrate particles have a number of negative charges on their surface to which the cations are attracted. The strength of the attraction depends on the cation, and in the case of horticulturally significant cations the most attractive is usually calcium, followed by magnesium, then by potassium, ammonium and finally sodium. The effect of these preferences is that when a more attractive cation becomes available the substrate will hold on to it and release an equivalent amount of a less attractive cation. There is usually a pH effect, with most substrates showing a higher CEC value at pH 7 than under more acidic conditions.

Cation exchange capacity can be used to supply nutrients to a crop by deliberately loading the substrate with suitable cations at the start of the crop so that they are gradually released to the roots. This is the basis of the nutrient-loaded zeolites described in chapter 6.

A substrate which has a significant cation exchange capacity, such as expanded clay aggregate or pumice, may start with its surface attachment points full, or 'loaded' with a range of cations, often predominantly sodium. When nutrient solution is first applied to it this sodium, which is at the bottom of the attractiveness scale, is released into the solution and replaced with other cations, especially calcium and magnesium. There is, therefore, a short period when the substrate is first used during which it causes an increase in sodium in the nutrient solution and a corresponding decrease in calcium and magnesium. This is normally a very transient effect, however, and has no significance in the longer term.

## Anion exchange

Clays and some other materials which demonstrate a high CEC value can also exchange anions, such as phosphate, sulphate and chloride. This is a much weaker characteristic and it is caused by an initial adsorption of phosphate on to the particles in combination with aluminium and iron, which can later be released if the pH changes substantially. This anion exchange capacity is not of any horticultural significance at the normal pH range.

The principle of plant sap analysis is very simple. As developed in Guernsey, it involves taking a representative 20g sample of fresh tissue, usually leaf stalks or whole leaves, and liquidising this with water to break open the tissue and release the soluble material. The resulting solution is then analysed as if it were a nutrient solution, and the levels of all the principal nutrients are expressed as mg/kg of fresh tissue. Other forms of extraction have been used, including pressing and freezing/thawing, and although the nutrient levels recorded for each are different, interpretation is achieved in much the same way.

Interpretating plant sap analysis results calls for considerable experience. Obvious deficiency or toxicity conditions are no problem because the analytical data will often be supported by visible symptoms. But for plant sap analysis to achieve its potential it has to be able to detect subtle trends and imbalances in the nutritional status of the crop long before they become visible, and before they have any adverse effect on crop performance.

Accurate sampling procedures and collecting samples at the same time of the day help to produce a reliable database of analytical results which form the basis of subsequent samples. In Guernsey more than 10,000 samples from about 30 different commercial crops have been analysed since the programme was set up in 1982.

Plant sap analysis is sufficiently sensitive to identify factors which have subtle but important effects on the performance of the crop. For example the way in which continued high humidity conditions around a crop can reduce the uptake of potassium and calcium but allow the supply of nitrate and phosphorus to continue unchecked. The technique has also proved valuable in identifying the importance of avoiding a sudden increase or decrease in the level of any nutrient in the substrate. It has shown that most crops can respond only slowly to such changes, and can suffer a severe nutrient imbalance during the acclimatisation period.

# 11 Fertilisers

*Chemical notation. Fertiliser ingredients. Nutrient solution concentrates. Two-tank and one-tank systems. Proprietary mixes.*

Plant nutritionalists and chemists use chemical symbols for nutrients as a shorthand notation. These symbols will also be found on laboratory reports and on fertiliser bags, as well as in this chapter. If you have not come across chemical symbols before the table identifying the meanings of those chemical symbols which are of horticultural interest will be useful.

## Chemical symbols

### Major nutrients

| | |
|---|---|
| $NO_3$-N | Nitrogen, in nitrate form |
| $NO_3$ | Nitrate |
| $NH_4$-N | Nitrogen, in ammonium form |
| $NH_4$ | Ammonium |
| N | Nitrogen in any form |
| $P_2O_5$ | Phosphate * |
| P | Phosphorus |
| $K_2O$ | Potash * |
| K | Potassium |
| Ca | Calcium |
| Mg | Magnesium |
| Na | Sodium |
| Cl | Chloride (or chlorine) |

*\* The terms 'phosphate' and 'potash' are seldom used in crop nutrition today, phosphorus and potassium being preferred*

### Minor nutrients*

| | |
|---|---|
| Fe | Iron |
| Cu | Copper |
| Zn | Zinc |
| Mn | Manganese |
| B | Boron |
| Mo | Molybdenum |
| Si | Silicon |

### Others

| | |
|---|---|
| $HCO_3$ | Bicarbonate |
| $CO_3$ | Carbonate |

*\* 'Minor nutrients' are those which are needed in relatively small amounts. They are also referred to as 'micronutrients' or 'trace elements'*

There are several ways of referring to the level of a nutrient in a solution. You may come across parts per million (ppm), milligrams per litre (mg/l), millimoles per litre (mmol/l or just mmol) or, less commonly, milli-equivalents (meq – see p75). The system which is used in the UK and North America and throughout this book is parts per million (ppm). Conversion to milligrams per litre (mg/l) is no problem because it is numerically exactly the same – 400 ppm is identical to 400 mg/litre.

## Conversion table – *mmol/litre to ppm (mg/litre)*

| *1 mmol/litre of nutrient =* | | *1 µmol/litre of nutrient =* | |
|---|---|---|---|
| *Nutrient* | *equals* | *Nutrient* | *equals* |
| $NO_3$-N | 14 ppm | Fe | 0.056 ppm |
| $NH_4$-N | 14 ppm | Cu | 0.064 ppm |
| Total N | 14 ppm | Zn | 0.065 ppm |
| P | 31 ppm | Mn | 0.055 ppm |
| K | 39 ppm | B | 0.011 ppm |
| Ca | 40 ppm | Mo | 0.096 ppm |
| Mg | 24 ppm | | |
| Na | 23 ppm | | |
| Cl | 35 ppm | | |
| $SO_4$-S | 32 ppm | | |
| $HCO_3$ | 61 ppm | | |

Millimoles per litre, or micromoles (µmol) per litre for low concentrations, are widely used units in the Netherlands, where a lot of advice on substrate growing originates. Avoid millimoles when you can, and if you cannot avoid them, use the conversion table to change them to ppm.

## FERTILISER INGREDIENTS

The raw materials for the production of nutrient solutions are horticultural fertilisers. A typical feed formulation will need about 12 to 15 ingredients out of the 20 or more fertilisers which are commonly used for this purpose. In most centres of horticultural production there should be no problem obtaining suitable fertilisers, but in isolated areas there are often difficulties. The major substrate production areas are generally very well served for fertiliser supply, and in Holland, for example, most of the principal materials are available in liquid form, as pre-dissolved and filtered concentrates.

It is important that the fertilisers which are used to make up feeds for use with substrates are clearly described as being of horticultural grade. This is particularly true for some of the major ingredients such as calcium nitrate and potassium sulphate, as agricultural grade fertilisers are also widely available which can give serious problems with impurities or poor solubility when they are used in the more demanding environment of substrate growing.

One way round fertiliser supply difficulties is to adopt a feeding programme which is based on a commercial material such as Solufeed (UK) or Hydrosol (USA). These provide most of the ingredients needed for a nutrient solution, and leave the grower to find only two or three of the more readily available fertilisers to complete the formulation. The disadvantage of this approach – apart from the fact that it is usually more expensive – is that it removes a lot of the flexibility which home-made formulations offer. The use of commercial mixes is described in more detail below.

The use of acids and alkalis such as nitric acid, phosphoric acid and potassium bicarbonate for the regulation of solution pH is described in chapter 8. It should be remembered that most of these materials also contribute to the total nutrient content of the final solution so they have to be taken into account when a feed is formulated.

## Acidity regulating acids and fertilisers

Nitric acid (62%)           13% N by weight, 18% by volume
Phosphoric acid (83%)       27% P by weight, 44% P by volume

Note: other strength acids are also available – adjust the nutrient
content accordingly. Use the 'volume' figure if measuring in
litres rather than kg.

Potassium bicarbonate    39% K
Sodium bicarbonate       27% Na

The nutrient content of all the commonly used fertiliser sources is given in the tables. It is important to note that in many cases there are two or more alternative forms of the fertiliser which have a different nutrient content. The nutrient content of any fertiliser should always be marked on the pack, so check this against the figure given in the table and make any necessary adjustments.

## Fertilisers supplying the major nutrients

| | |
|---|---|
| Ammonium nitrate | 17% $NO_3$-N, 17% $NH_4$-N |
| Calcium chloride | 29% Ca, 51% Cl |
| Calcium nitrate | 14% $NO_3$-N, 1% $NH_4$-N, 19% Ca |
| Magnesium nitrate | 9% Mg, 11% $NO_3$-N |
| Magnesium sulphate | 10% Mg, 13% $SO_4$-S |
| Mono ammonium phosphate | 27% P, 12% $NH_4$-N |
| Mono potassium phosphate | 23% P, 28% K |
| Potassium chloride | 50% K, 50% Cl |
| Potassium nitrate | 13% $NO_3$-N     38% K |
| Potassium sulphate | 45% K, 18% $SO_4$-S |
| Sodium chloride | 39% Na, 61% Cl |
| Urea | 47% N |

## Fertilisers supplying chelated iron

| | |
|---|---|
| DTPA | 7 or 9% Fe |
| EDDHA | 5 or 6% Fe |
| EDTA | 3% Fe |

## Fertilisers supplying micronutrients

| | |
|---|---|
| Ammonium heptamolybdate | 58% Mo |
| Borax | 11% B |
| Copper sulphate | 25% Cu |
| Manganese sulphate | 32% Mn |
| Sodium molybdate | 40% Mo |
| Solubor (proprietary product) | 21% B |
| Zinc sulphate | 23% or 36% Zn |

*Chelated forms of several micronutrients are also available – refer to text for their nutrient content.*

Micronutrients can also be obtained in complex organic forms including extracts from seaweed, plants, algae or brown coal. It is often claimed that micronutrients in this form are more available to the crop and are therefore superior to inorganic ionic nutrients. However a trial in Holland demonstrated that if anything the reverse is true, and that ionic micronutrients with the possible exception of iron are taken up more reliably than organic complexes.

There are also chelated forms of most micronutrients. In this case there does seem to be some merit in their use, particularly under variable pH conditions. This is because under these conditions the relatively large amount of chelated iron present in most feeds can switch its chelation to any other ionic micronutrients which are present in the solution, leaving a substantial part of the iron vulnerable to loss by precipitation.

## NUTRIENT SOLUTION CONCENTRATES

The need for a two-tank nutrient dilution system for substrate growing was described in chapter 7. This is a universal requirement, irrespective of which substrate is used or what type of growing system it is used in. The only exceptions are where a dilute nutrient solution is made up directly by dissolving individual nutrients into the final volume of water or where a one-tank system (see below) is used. Neither of these alternatives is really suitable for commercial scale crop production however.

Both calcium and phosphate must be supplied continuously to an inert growing medium. If they are mixed as concentrates then they combine to form an insoluble product with disastrous consequences. Two tanks are therefore used to hold the concentrate fertilisers, one for all of the calcium sources and the other for all of the phosphate sources. If sulphates are used these too must be kept apart from the calcium source, so they are put into the second tank.

Other non-reactive fertilisers can be put into either tank, although there are particular conventions which are widely adopted. For example the chelated iron source is commonly put into the calcium tank so that it is kept apart from any ionic micronutrients, which go into the other tank. The calcium tank is, by convention, referred to as the 'A tank', while the tank containing phosphates and sulphates is referred to as the 'B tank'.

It is usual to make up stock solutions, or concentrates, at one hundred times the desired final strength, and to dilute these stock solutions separately at a rate of about 1:100 before combining them to produce the nutrient solution which is fed to the crop. Dilution can be done using a fixed ratio diluter (proportioner) or injector or a more elaborate variable rate system, the latter type commonly being under computer control.

If the dilution rate is set by a conductivity controller the stock solutions are still made up at approximately one hundred times strength.

Once the fertilisers have been diluted to their final concentration calcium, phosphate and sulphate can be safely mixed, although even then there is some risk of precipitation in some circumstances particularly if high pH conditions occur in the irrigation lines.

Nitric acid can be put into either of the stock solution tanks or into a separate tank. If potassium bicarbonate is used this should be supplied from a separate tank. If nitric acid is included in the stock solutions for pH regulation, it is a good idea to put half of the required volume into each tank. This creates more favourable conditions for dissolving the other fertilisers. This cannot done with phosphoric acid, because this must be kept apart from the calcium source. Phosphoric acid can be put either into the stock tank which does not contain calcium or into a separate tank.

### Formulating concentrates

The calculations which go into formulating nutrient solution concentrates for substrates are not difficult to carry out but they are tedious, and growers are recommended to have the job done by someone else – fertiliser supplier, adviser or consultant — if possible. If it is necessary to formulate nutrient solution concentrate solutions given only the ppm of each nutrient to be supplied in the dilute solution, the following brief description may help:

### *GROUND RULES TO FORMULATE NUTRIENT CONCENTRATE*
- Calculate the amount of acid or alkali needed and work out what contribution this makes to other nutrients (N, P, K)

- Calculate how much P must be included in addition to the above. Work out how much P fertiliser to use, and what other nutrients it provides (K or N)

● Calculate how much calcium to add, either as nitrate or chloride, and what other nutrients this will provide (N, Cl)

● Work out how much more N you want. Include ammonium nitrate if needed, then supply the rest as potassium nitrate

● Calculate the remaining K requirement as potassium chloride

● Calculate the requirement for magnesium and micronutrients

● Divide the fertilisers between the two tanks as follows:

| **TANK A:** | **TANK B:** |
|---|---|
| Calcium nitrate | Potassium nitrate (half) |
| Calcium chloride | Potassium chloride (half) |
| Potassium nitrate (half) | Phosphorus source |
| Potassium chloride (half) | Magnesium source |
| Iron chelate | Other micronutrients |

The weight or volume of each fertiliser which should go into a concentrate solution for dilution at 1:100 is calculated from the tables of fertilisers. For example if the aim is to have a nutrient solution containing 150 ppm of calcium, using calcium chloride:

150 ppm is 150mg/litre, so a one hundred times strength stock solution must contain –
100 x 150mg, or 15g/litre of calcium. 15g/litre is 15kg of calcium/1,000 litres

Calcium chloride contains 29% calcium, so the amount of this fertiliser needed to supply 15kg of calcium is –
15 x 100 ÷ 29 = 52kg/1,000 litres
This is the amount of calcium chloride which should be added to Tank A

Calcium chloride also contains 51% chloride, so 52kg/1,000 litres of this material contains –
52 x 51 ÷ 100 = 26kg of chloride
Diluted at 1:100 this will add 260 ppm of chloride to the final nutrient solution

Working back from these calculations, 10kg of any fertiliser put into 1,000 litres of stock solution for dilution at 1:100 will give its % content as ppm

So 10kg of calcium chloride (29% Ca) in 1,000 litres of solution at 1:100 will give 29 ppm of calcium

In areas of intensive horticulture like Holland it is possible to obtain pre-dissolved and filtered individual fertiliser concentrates. These can be stored in separate tanks and pumped to the stock tanks as they are needed to ensure an accurate mix of the required fertilisers without any problems of insoluble residues. If these materials are available it is also possible to go one step further and design a fully flexible computer-controlled dilution system which draws from each of the individual fertiliser concentrates according to the demands of the crop. This avoids the problem of having to wait until a batch of stock solutions has been used up before the feed formulation can be changed.

Current research in Holland is now looking one stage further still. If changes to the feed formulation can be made on demand it should be possible to fully automate a closed system so that any deficit in the nutrient content of the circulating solution is detected and immediately corrected. The problem here is that while it is relatively easy to measure the level of each nutrient in a solution in the laboratory it is not so easily done on the nursery. Each nutrient has to be continuously monitored by a device known as an ion-selective electrode (ISE). At present there are effective ISEs for only some of the nutrients which would have to be monitored, and until all of the nutrients in the circulating solution can be measured full automatic correction will not be possible. Even then there may prove to be difficulties with the reliability and long-term performance of the ISEs.

# One-tank mixes

Multi-tank systems are the only satisfactory answer to the complexity of feeding commercial crops growing in substrates. However it sometimes happens that a grower would like to try out a substrate or a growing system on a small scale without having to set up a complex dilution system in the early stages. For this purpose, or for the enthusiatic amateur grower who would like to produce a small crop in a substrate system, the one tank feed comes into its own.

The one tank feed is the exception to the rule that concentrated calcium and phosphorus-containing nutrient solutions have to be kept apart. This feed is able to get round this difficulty because it holds the phosphorus in a complex called acid magnesium phosphate (AMP), in which form it can exist in a concentrated solution together with calcium without combining with it.

There are two disadvantages with a one-tank mix based on AMP. One is that the mix is inflexible, allowing no variation in the ratio of magnesium or phosphorus nor, once made up, in the levels of micronutrients. The other is that, being quite strongly acidic, it cannot be used with rainwater or any other very pure water source. Used at normal strength an AMP mix will neutralise about 40 ppm of bicarbonate (see chapter 7), and if less bicarbonate than this is present in the water supply it will lower the solution pH to an unacceptable level.

The acid magnesium phosphate stock solution which is the basis of the one tank mix is best prepared commercially because it involves the use of concentrated acid and the procedure generates a lot of heat and frothing. Once the stock has been produced it can be diluted with water, combined with suitable amounts of calcium and potassium fertilisers, and used in a simple one-stage dilutor or injector to produce a dilute complete nutrient solution. Changes in the formulation of the dilute feed are only possible by changing the amounts of calcium or potassium which are added to the AMP stock.

## PROPRIETARY MIXES

Many growers using substrates rely on proprietary fertiliser mixes to supply at least a part of the crop's nutrient requirements. Although this option is almost always more expensive than using straight fertilisers it does have a number of benefits. In particular it simplifies the job of constructing the stock concentrates by reducing the number of individual ingredients in the mix. Proprietary mixes, apart from providing most or all of the major nutrients, usually have a full complement of micronutrients.

The most popular proprietary fertiliser mix in the UK, Solufeed, contains many of the individual fertilisers needed to make up a complete nutrient solution, but still requires the grower to add calcium, potassium and, for some crops, some additional iron. While this increases the effort the grower has to make, it has the advantage that it allows the finished feed to be more precisely tailored to the crop and the circumstances. Proprietary products are always a compromise, and the greater the gain in simplicity, the greater the loss of flexibility.

In North America many growers use the product Hydrosol as the main constituent of their nutrient mix for substrates. Like Solufeed, Hydrosol contains a balanced mix of the major nutrients other than calcium, in this case with the full potassium requirement, and also has the full range of micronutrients. Again the grower has to provide calcium fertilisers to make up the tank A solution.

It is important to emphasise the limitations of proprietary mixes where the grower does not also have ready access to straight fertilisers. If, for example, the raw water supply contains variable nutrient levels and has a variable pH adjustment demand, then some flexibility in the nutrient supply in the feed is an advantage. Similarly if the nutrient levels in the substrate get out of balance, especially in a recirculating system, quite substantial changes may have to be made to the feeding programme to restore the balance. This can be a particular problem in the case of micronutrient levels.

# 12 Reusing substrates

*Reusing and recycling substrates. Sterilising techniques. Disposal of used substrates.*

Rockwool is a relatively stable substrate, and slabs with a density of 70 or 80kg/cu m can be used either for a single long-term crop like roses or carnations or for a series of at least two or three shorter crops. Lower density rockwool slabs and blocks are usually recommended for single season use, but even these can be re-used at least once if they are handled with care.

There is some evidence that re-used rockwool slabs can produce marginally better crops in their second year than new slabs. In some cases this may be because the residual organic matter in the re-used slabs provides a better root environment.

Rockwool slabs intended for replanting are in most cases sterilised by steam to destroy any disease organisms present. Some growers replant without sterilising the rockwool if the previous crop has been particularly free from root diseases but this is too risky to be generally recommended.

## Steam sterilisation

Steam sterilisation does not have a substantial effect on the structure of the slabs, but it does break down some of the bonding and cause a slight reduction in slab height. This can become significant after repeated sterilisation and the loss of height can then be enough to limit the number of times the slabs can be reused. A 7.5cm slab can generally be expected to retain the minimum safe height of 6cm for at least three annual crops. The economics of reuse compared to replacement need to be considered before a decision is made, and this calculation should include not only the cost of sterilisation against the cost of new slabs but also the fact that the labour input for sterilising and re-using slabs is almost twice that which is needed for slab replacement.

For steam sterilisation to adequately control soil-borne disease organisms the full volume of each slab should be heated to a temperature of at least 70C and held at this temperature for at least 30 minutes. This is the minimum effective treatment, however, and it is not enough to kill viruses such as TMV or cucumber virus. If virus disease is a problem aim to achieve 100C for at least 15 minutes. In practice slabs are usually heated to 100C for 15 minutes or more as a matter of course. (In high summer light areas an alternative to sterilisation is solarisation – see p131.)

To keep the cost of sterilisation as low as possible and to be sure of doing a good job the rockwool slabs should be as dry as possible before steaming. The best way to achieve this is to reduce the irrigation rate at the end of the crop to allow the plants to draw as much water as possible out of the substrate. This avoids having to handle wet slabs, which is likely to cause some mechanical damage to at least a proportion of them. If this is not possible or if some wet slabs remain, the only other effective option is to dry them against the heating pipes.

The slabs should also be free of residual salts at the end of the crop. At the end of the season there is likely to be a build-up of ions such as sodium, chloride and sulphate in the rockwool. If the irrigation rate is to be reduced during the last week or two of the crop this will have the effect of concentrating these salts still further to the detriment of the following crop.

The solution to this in the case of a non-recirculating system is to precede the drying out phase with a week or two of considerable over-watering to flush out as much salt as possible. In a recirculating system the same end can be achieved by removing and replacing a substantial proportion of the circulating volume at the same stage. At the same time the feed concentration should be reduced to a minimum for the remainder of the season, using the best quality water available.

Once the slabs are dry they have to be unwrapped and the old crop has to be removed as carefully as possible. If the top surface of the slabs is damaged during this operation there could be problems establishing the following crop.

With some weak-rooted crops the plants can be removed cleanly by twisting them off the surface. If this does not work the old crop will have to be cut off at slab level with a heavy knife. At one time the usual technique was to accept a certain amount of damage to the surface of the slab and to turn it upside down for the second crop. This is now seldom done, firstly because high density rockwool is generally used for more than two crops, and secondly because many growers are now using fibre-gradient slabs which will not perform properly upside down.

## Pallet loading

A few growers sheet steam the whole glasshouse area with the rockwool slabs in situ, but this is an ineffective and extravagant way of sterilising the substrate even though it may also help to clean the glasshouse floor covering and equipment at the same time. Most growers stack the unwrapped slabs on pallets, leaving appropriate air spaces, and inject steam under a heavy polyethylene tarpaulin. A typical wooden pallet will accommodate about 140 standard size slabs stacked 20 high. Any slabs which are still wet should be kept to one side so that they can be put together on a separate pallet and given a longer steaming time. Thermometer probes should be placed deep within the stack before it is covered to monitor the progress of the steaming operation.

A full pallet of fairly dry slabs can generally be brought up to 100C throughout the stack within about an hour, after which they should be kept at this temperature for a further 15 minutes. Moderately wet slabs may need 2 or 3 hours to achieve the target temperature throughout the stack.

Some larger rockwool growers in Holland put several pallets together in a large sealable container into which steam is injected. Custom built containers are available with an extractor fan to draw the steam more quickly through the stack and speed up the operation. With this system, which even works well with wet rockwool, it is not necessary to have gaps between the individual slabs.

After steaming, the slabs are re-wrapped and placed out in the glasshouse ready to be wetted up for the new crop. The polyethylene used for wrapping should be opaque; it is usual to use black/white co-extruded material with the white side outwards for maximum light reflectance.

If the slabs are of the fibre-gradient type – which can only be effectively used one way up – it is important to handle the slabs in such a way that their orientation is not changed during drying, steam sterilising, wrapping or replacing in the glasshouse. *The top surface of these slabs cannot be recognised by eye once the wrap has been removed.*

## REUSING OTHER SUBSTRATES

*Glasswool slabs* are steam sterilised in exactly the same way as rockwool. The only difference of any note is that they are rather easier to dry out at the end of the crop. Their more open structure and lower water-holding capacity means that if they are stood on end for a short time most of the residual water will drain out. The rest can then be removed by drying on heating pipes.

*Polyurethane foam slabs*, like rockwool, are easily and safely sterilised by steam. The slabs should be dried out as far as possible before steaming, using the same techniques described for rockwool slabs. The structural characteristics of polyurethane foam makes it easy to remove any excess water at the end of the season. If it has not been taken out by the plants by the end of the crop, then it can be squeezed out by hand or mechanically. Slabs which remain wet can also be placed lengthways along warm heating pipes to dry them. They will be distorted during this operation but they will return to their original shape as soon as they are wetted. After they have been steam sterilised the slabs are simply re-wrapped and placed out in the glasshouse ready to be wetted up for the new crop. The wrap should be big enough to allow for the fact that, unlike rockwool, foam slabs swell in every dimension by about 10 to 15% when wetted. A 100cm long slab should therefore be housed in a wrap which is at least 120cm long. A similar margin should be allowed for expansion of the width and height of the slab, so a 15cm wide slab will generally be put into a 25cm wide sleeve. Homogenous polyurethane foam slabs are much softer and flexible than bonded foam slabs, so should be handled with care during recycling if they are to be used several times.

Granulate substrates like *expanded clay aggregates, perlite* and *sand* which are used in open troughs can be steam sterilised in situ but the operating parameters must be selected to match the physical characteristics of the substrate. Light, open materials like perlite and clay aggregates, for example, offer very little resistance to the passage of steam through them, so they need to be sterilised at low pressure with an effective cover. These substrates can also be sterilised from above if there is a drainage pipe in the base of the trough. Heavy materials like sand are more of a problem, and these will generally be sterilised either from below or using a suction system to draw the steam more quickly through the substrate. Light materials like perlite can also be removed from the growing system, particularly if this consists of individual bags or buckets, and steamed in large containers with injection points in the base.

## Disposal of substrates

The structural stability of many substrates can become a disadvantage when they reach the end of their effective life. The enormous volume of rockwool slabs discarded by growers every year, for example, does not have any obvious value outside the horticultural industry.

On a small scale rockwool slabs can be broken down and used as an agricultural or domestic soil conditioning material, but the volume which can be used in this way is comparatively small. Re-use as a constituent of potting compost can also use only a very small proportion of the waste product. The only realistic option is to add used slabs back into the rockwool manufacturing process. This is an acceptable solution provided the proportion of recycled rockwool to raw ingredients is not too high, and when it is done the quality of the end product does not appear to differ from that which is produced only from raw materials.

The disposal of spent rockwool slabs from the extensive horticultural industry in the Westland of Holland was an embarrassment for some years. The rockwool manufacturers became involved to try to solve the problem by taking back used slabs for recycling. However this proved to be more difficult than expected and for some time they had to reject unwanted slabs because the stockpile awaiting treatment was too great. In the last couple of years the technical difficulties involved in breaking down the old rockwool and incorporating it in the production of new rockwool have for the most part been solved, and growers once again have an outlet for their used slabs.

# Part 3 Crop production in rockwool

## 13 Tomatoes

*Propagation. Layout and preparation. Irrigation and nutrition. Nutrition problems.*

Most tomato crops in Europe and North America are now grown in rockwool, although perlite is a popular alternative in Scotland and the north of England. A number of growers in Holland and Belgium have been using some alternative substrates, particularly polyurethane foam, for several years. The techniques for growing most major types of tomatoes – round, beefsteak and plum – are very similar, and these notes apply to all of them. Cherry tomatoes need a rather higher conductivity feeding programme throughout the cropping period to control plant vigour and maximise fruit quality, but they are otherwise managed in a similar way.

### EQUIPMENT

The equipment requirements for tomatoes in rockwool are described in chapter 2. The irrigation needs of the crop are such that the installation should be capable of applying up to 25 waterings per day at an irrigation rate of between 1.3 and 1.5 litres/drip nozzle/hour. Irrigation control is usually either by light integration or by start trays – see chapter 9. Simple time clock control is not very satisfactory, although there are acceptable control systems which are based on a time clock but which can vary the quantity applied per cycle according to the time of day. Whatever system is used, frequent monitoring of the slab conductivity followed by appropriate adjustments to the feeding and irrigation programme are essential, particularly early in the season.

Accurate feeding is needed so simple barrel type dilutors are not adequate. Fixed ratio feed injectors can be used but the changing conductivity and nutrient ratio requirements of tomatoes means that stock solutions have to be frequently modified. A better option is to use variable ratio injectors, preferably under computer control. Because tomatoes demand more frequent changes in either the constituents or the conductivity of the feed solution than most other crops they are an ideal subject for the multiple tank feeding systems which are now becoming available. In these, several of the individual fertilisers which are normally combined to form the two stock solutions in a traditional feeding system are kept in separate tanks and can be independently added to or withdrawn from the dilute feed. This makes it possible to modify the input solution easily without having to construct a new formulation of stock solution each time.

## PLANT PROPAGATION

In the main tomato production areas propagation is usually carried out by specialist plant raisers, but there is no reason why it should not be done on the nursery if suitable facilities are available. Tomato plants for planting out on to rockwool slabs are always propagated in rockwool cubes, although the germination stage is sometimes carried out in peat plugs for subsequent transplanting into rockwool immediately after seedling emergence. A typical rockwool cube for sowing is 3 to 4cm square and a similar height, containing a shallow hole about 1cm in diameter in the top surface to take the seed.

After the seedlings have emerged these cubes are placed into larger rockwool blocks, usually about 6 to 7cm square. These have a square hole in the top which is just big enough to take the sowing cubes.

Some growers use slabs of smaller cubes for the germination stage, down to 2cm square. These are particularly well suited to mechanical seed sowing, but they have to be moved on to the next stage more quickly after emergence.

Larger propagation blocks are sometimes used for the later stages of plant raising, up to 10cm square. These have the advantage that the plants can be moved into the growing house a little later provided sufficient space is available to hold them in the propagation area without overcrowding.

Tomato plants raised through the winter benefit from supplementary lighting, and high intensity sodium lamps are often used over the benches to give 2,500 lux at seedling height for up to16 hour days. Maintaining the optimum spacing on the bench makes this option more economical.

### Setting out sowing cubes

The sowing cubes should be placed out touching, either in trays or on a solid level surface which has been covered with polyethylene film to allow uniform irrigation and drainage. Between 650 and 900 cubes 3–4cm square will occupy a cubic metre of bed, depending on the precise dimensions of the cubes.

The sowing medium should be thoroughly wetted before use with a nutrient solution with a conductivity of 2.5mS/cm (see p92 for formulation). The blocks into which the seedlings will be transferred should be similarly wetted before use with a nutrient solution with a conductivity of between 2.5 and 3.5mS/cm. The conductivity should be selected to match the growing conditions. For dark conditions in short days use the higher end of the conductivity range, and use a progressively weaker feed in better natural light or when supplementary lighting is employed.

Tomato seed is sown individually into the blocks and the holes are then lightly filled with a material such as perlite or vermiculite to maintain moist conditions around the seed until it has germinated. Alternatively the holes can remain open and the blocks covered over with polyethylene film to retain enough moisture for germination. Further watering should not be necessary until after emergence, which will occur within three or four days. Then three or four applications of the same strength nutrient solution should be generously applied over the top of the cubes during the period until the cubes are moved on to the larger blocks.

The temperature within the cubes should be kept up during the germination stage to minimise the proportion of rogue seedlings. A minimum of 20C to 22C is usually recommended until seedling emergence. Under-bench heating is an efficient way of achieving this if the facility is available. If heat is applied below the cubes then it is important to monitor the water content of the rockwool to avoid any drying out. If the blocks dry back the remaining nutrient solution within them will be concentrated and this will have an adverse effect on the development of the root system. Later on in the propagation period the night temperature can gradually be reduced to 16C or 17C, with the day temperature set at between 18C and 21C according to the growing conditions.

## Setting out propagation blocks

The larger propagation blocks should be set out in the same way as the sowing cubes, at a density of approximately 100/sq m. Some blocks are now made with grooved bases to prevent the base of the blocks from sealing on to the surface of the bench. Grooved blocks do not need to be stood on perlite, as any surplus drainage is effectively carried away from the blocks in the grooves even if they are placed directly on to a polyethylene sheet. Avoiding the need for perlite has the advantage that it reduces the number of roots which escape from the base of the blocks and which are often damaged when the plants are moved. Grooved blocks should be placed with the grooves running down the slope, both in the propagation area and when standing the plants on to the slabs.

The blocks should be supplied at first with nutrient solution at a conductivity of around 3.0mS/cm, gradually increasing as the plants grow. In northern European conditions a conductivity of between 4.0 and 5.5mS/cm should be achieved by the time the plants come into flower. Depending on the temperature regime the cubes will be ready to be placed into the larger blocks about two weeks after sowing. They can be ready as soon as 10 days after sowing in good conditions with supplementary lighting and carbon dioxide enrichment.

The sowing cubes should not be put into the larger blocks until the seedlings are well rooted, otherwise the roots will not be able to move quickly down to reach the lower water level in the blocks.

Once the plants are in the larger blocks, irrigation should be carefully controlled to keep the blocks moist but not overwet. As a general guide the blocks are likely to need watering once every two or three days at first, increasing to once every day by the end of the propagation stage. Monitoring the water content of the blocks is best done by weighing a few representative blocks at regular intervals. An application of no more than 100ml of nutrient solution should be given to each block on each occasion, and the frequency of watering should be adjusted to keep the weight of each cube within the range 300 to 400g. A 100ml application will increase the weight of each block by 100g.

The conductivity of the nutrient solution which is applied during this stage should be matched to light levels, and gradually increased to give the required conductivity at planting time (see above). In very good natural light, or with high level supplementary lighting, a conductivity of 2.5mS/cm is adequate. In very poor light the conductivity can be set as high as 6.0mS/cm, but not higher. In most cases a conductivity of between 3.0 and 5.0mS/cm will be used. The solution within the blocks will rise above that used for irrigation. This is acceptable, but it should not be allowed to exceed 10.0mS/cm or root damage may be caused.

Monitor the conductivity of the nutrient solution in the blocks frequently by gently squeezing the solution out of a few blocks and measuring it with a portable conductivity meter.

As the plants grow and their leaves start to overlap, the blocks should be spaced out. At about four weeks they will need a density no higher than 30 to 40 plants/sq m, decreasing to about 20 plants/sq m after a further week. At this stage, and particularly if supplementary lighting is not available, the blocks can be moved into the growing house and placed out on the slabs at their final density of 2 to 3 plants/sq m.

## LAYOUT AND PREPARATION

The guidelines for preparing the glasshouse and setting out rockwool slabs in either a closed or an open system are given in chapter 7. Tomatoes benefit from an adequate substrate temperature so setting the slabs on to polystyrene to isolate them from the glasshouse floor is worthwhile. If under-slab heating can be provided, so much the better, although experimental evidence indicates that root zone warming for tomatoes gives only marginal benefits in most circumstances, and may only be economic in particularly cold climates or when glasshouse heating costs are particularly high.

Warming the irrigation water can be an effective way of avoiding low slab temperatures in the absence of root zone warming, but the solution temperature should not be above 22C.

Based on a typical crop density of 2.5 plants/sq m of glasshouse, the minimum safe volume of rockwool for tomatoes is 10 litres/sq m, which is equivalent to 4 litres/plant. This is the minimum volume, and it is safe only if the irrigation system is particularly accurate. If the irrigation system is less reliable 12 or even 15 litres/sq m should be allowed.

The standard rockwool slab for vegetable crops, 90 or 100cm long, 15cm wide and 7.5cm high, will therefore take two plants, providing a little over 5 litres/plant. A 120cm long slab will take three plants based on the standard plant spacing for tomatoes of 2.5 to 3 plants/sq m, giving 4.5 litres of rockwool per plant. The slabs may be touching end-to-end along the row or spaced with gaps, depending on the slab length and the required plant spacing in the row. Pairs of slabs in a single wrap are often used for tomatoes.

Both high and low density rockwool is suitable for tomatoes. A trial at Naaldwijk in Holland using various sources of slabs found yield differences of only 1 to 2% between different grades and different manufacturers.

Reused slabs, provided they are clean and structurally sound, are satisfactory. They have actually been shown to give slightly higher yields than new slabs in some trials, perhaps because the residue of roots left in the slab from the previous crop improves its water holding capacity slightly. High density rockwool is more likely to withstand repeated reuse than lower density materials because of the effects of handling and sterilising the slabs on their physical structure. Techniques for steam sterilising rockwool slabs for reuse are given in chapter 12.

Wrapped slabs are preferred to bare slabs for strong rooting crops like tomatoes because without a polyethylene sleeve to contain them the roots tend to follow a path down to the drainage channels. Once they have done this they encounter a nutrient solution which is quite different to that in the slabs, and which can dry up intermittently causing root stress or damage. Wrapping the slabs in polyethylene either singly or in pairs largely prevents this from happening.

The slabs can either be laid out in double rows between the paths, or in a single row at closer spacing if the crop is to be trained on the V system.

The slabs must be thoroughly wetted through before planting using nutrient solution with a conductivity similar to that which the plants will be receiving at planting (see below). This will usually be around 4.0 to 5.0mS/cm for January plantings in northern European conditions and proportionally lower for later plantings.

The best way to ensure adequate wetting is to cut out the planting holes, place the irrigation nozzles in or over the holes, and to water to saturation. About 12 litres per standard slab will be needed and even then it may be necessary to top up any dry slabs by hand. At this stage the slabs should not be slit for drainage. Wetting should be done at least a day or two before planting, and preferably before the plants are placed on the slabs so that the temperature within the rockwool can rise to that of the air.

## Planting out

Planting is carried out when the flowers on the first truss are showing colour, about seven or eight weeks after sowing under average growing conditions. Delaying the planting beyond this stage is likely to have an adverse effect on the development of a strong root system in the slabs, and this will be translated into reduced fruit size on the second and third bunches. It can also lead to root problems in early spring if the root volume is insufficient to cope with the sudden spells of hot weather which are common at this time.

Planting is achieved simply by placing each block so that it is in firm contact with the exposed surface of the rockwool slab, at the same time moving the drip from the slab into the block. The blocks can be more firmly attached to the slabs by pegging or by leaving a loop of polyethylene when cutting the planting hole and passing this over the top of the block. This is particularly important if the bottom ends of the crop support strings are fixed in place by running them between the bottom of the block and the surface of the slab.

For the first few days after planting only small volumes of water should be used, as the slabs are at this stage still undrained and have a high water level to aid rooting out of the blocks. Large volumes of water at this stage will lower the temperature within the slabs to the detriment of root development.

When drainage is established a few days after planting by making diagonal slits between the plants, the frequency and volume of irrigation can be gradually increased. Two diagonal drainage slits should be made in each slab, preferably spaced on the lower edge of the slab and between rather than under the plants. It is important that the slits are made right down to the base so that no reservoir of solution is left in the bottom of the slabs.

Although the financial benefits of substrate heating are not convincing for tomatoes, it is important at this stage to avoid applying very cold nutrient solution to the plants. This is because the added volume of solution is large compared to the volume of rockwool and the root system can be damaged by the sudden temperature reduction.

If possible the dilute nutrient solution, or the water used to prepare it, should be kept in a holding tank within the glasshouse before it is used so that it can equilibrate with the air temperature. Alternatively it is possible to set up a simple heating unit for the input solution to bring its temperature up to the air temperature in the glasshouse.

## IRRIGATION

Suitable irrigation systems for vegetable production in rockwool slabs are described in chapter 9, as are the alternative ways of controlling and monitoring irrigation frequency and volume. Whichever method of irrigation control is adopted – solar integration, evaporation sensors or start trays – the aim must be to initiate each irrigation cycle when it is needed and to provide the required volume accurately and consistently. The irrigation regime may need to be adjusted to the density of the rockwool slab. High density slabs hold slightly more water than lower density ones so they should be watered rather less frequently.

Tomatoes in rockwool will typically be irrigated with between 80 and 125ml of water each time and up to 25 times a day. Very small applied volumes should be avoided because they tend to keep the rockwool too wet. They are also more difficult to apply accurately and consistently. The maximum demand per plant during periods of rapid growth in the summer can be as high as 2.5 litres/day plus an allowance for drainage. An indication of the irrigation demand of a rockwool tomato crop is given in chapter 8.

## NUTRITION

The formulation of a suitable nutrient solution for tomatoes must take into account both the target conductivity and the nutrient contribution of the raw water source. The ratios between nutrients in the basic summer feed, which is used at a conductivity of about 2.0mS/cm, are different to those which are used to produce higher conductivities early in the season. The table (p92) illustrates current thinking for feeding tomatoes in rockwool and particularly takes into account recent evidence that increased chloride levels are preferable to high nitrate levels when high conductivity solutions are being formulated.

The environmental problems of high nitrate levels in the drainage solution has led to a lot of research into the use of alternatives, particularly sulphate and chloride. Neither sulphate nor chloride have been shown to have any specific adverse effects on the crop.

The quality and solubility of commercial sulphate fertilisers is often a problem so the substitution of nitrate by chloride has become the standard, especially for high conductivity feeds. This also has a financial bonus as the cost of chloride fertilisers is a lot less than nitrate fertilisers. In Europe the cost of potassium supplied as chloride is about half that of potassium supplied as nitrate.

There is evidence that the nitrogen level in the substrate can be reduced to well below 100 ppm without any adverse effect on the growth or vigour of the crop, but commercial recommendations are at present set at a minimum of around 120 ppm in the slab solution during the summer to provide a safety margin.

The use of either potassium chloride or calcium chloride as a constituent of tomato feeds has actually proved to have a beneficial effect on the uptake of calcium by the crop and to reduce the incidence of blossom end rot and related disorders. Taken too far, however, it can increase the incidence of gold speck.

There is also some evidence that very high chloride levels may have a slight adverse effect on fruit firmness, so an excessive build-up of chloride in the slab solution, particularly in recirculation systems, should be avoided.

## Conductivity

The very high chloride feed levels which are required at conductivities of 4.0mS/cm and above are less important as the irrigation volume which is used early in the year in conjunction with high conductivity feeds is usually small. There is no evidence that wetting up the rockwool slabs with a high chloride solution gives any problems, but equally there is no reason why higher nitrate levels cannot be used at this stage because there is little or no drainage from the substrate. At the start of the season, to assist in keeping a high total conductivity, the substrate chloride level can safely go as high as 900 ppm but later in the year it should be kept below about 500 ppm.

It has been demonstrated that high conductivity feeds can be achieved by leaving all the major nutrients at their summer levels and incorporating sodium chloride into the feed to increase the conductivity. This seems to work well, although it has not been widely accepted commercially. With this option, the effect of any particular conductivity increase on growth restriction is greater than when nutrient addition is used so the target conductivity at each stage should be rather lower.

## Typical input solutions for tomatoes

| Conductivity (mS/cm) | | 2.0 | 3.0 | 4.0 | 5.0 |
|---|---|---|---|---|---|
| $NO_3$-N | (ppm) | 175 | 250 | 300 | 350 |
| $NH_4$-N | (ppm) | 7 | 7 | 7 | 7 |
| P | (ppm) | 30 | 30 | 30 | 30 |
| K | (ppm) | 275 | 420 | 600 | 750 |
| Ca | (ppm) | 160 | 250 | 340 | 420 |
| Mg | (ppm) | 50 | 70 | 100 | 120 |
| Cl | (ppm) | 35 | 320 | 500 | 750 |

| Micronutrients | |
|---|---|
| Fe | 1.50 ppm |
| Cu | 0.05 ppm |
| Zn | 0.50 ppm |
| Mn | 0.75 ppm |
| B | 0.40 ppm |
| Mo | 0.10 ppm |

*See chapter 10 for information on formulation, effects of raw water quality and the use of ammonium nitrogen for pH control*

After planting, the conductivity of the feed solution is matched to the growing conditions and to the stage of development of the crop. A starting level of about 5.0mS/cm will be used for most early crops under northern European light conditions, and this will be reduced in a series of small steps down to 2.0 or 2.5mS/cm by early summer. The conductivity then remains at the same level until shortly before the crop is cleared, when it can be increased to 3.5 or 4.0mS/cm to improve fruit quality at the end of the crop. The basic summer feed can go down to 2.0mS/cm only if the water quality is high. If the conductivity of the water is above about 0.5mS/cm, then the feed should be made up to 2.5mS/cm to ensure an adequate supply of nutrients.

Cherry tomatoes in rockwool should be grown at a continuous high conductivity to ensure good fruit quality. It has been demonstrated that, as with other types of tomatoes, a high conductivity feed for cherry tomatoes can be formulated economically and safely by using calcium and potassium chlorides in place of nitrates. The input solution conductivity for cherry tomatoes will generally be in the range 3.0 to 4.0mS/cm, with the aim of maintaining a slab conductivity of around 4.5 to 6.0mS/cm. If the acidity level of the fruit is insufficient for good flavour then the conductivity should be increased towards the top end of this range. This is also the way to deal with over-large fruit. As with round tomatoes, it is also possible to generate the higher conductivities need for cherry tomatoes by using sodium chloride. A feed conductivity of 3.0mS/cm throughout the season will usually be adequate in this case.

As with all crops the substrate solution for tomatoes should be checked frequently and the irrigation regime changed if necessary to keep the conductivity in the slabs no more than 0.5 to 1.0mS/cm above that of the feed solution. The substrate pH should be kept within the range 5.5 to 6.0 by acidifying the input solution down to a bicarbonate content of about 50 ppm and if necessary by adjusting the ammonium content of the nutrient solution (see chapter 10).

Ideally new slabs should be wetted up at a slightly lower pH to allow for the initial alkaline reaction of the new rockwool, but this is seldom carried out in practice.

## Nutritional problems

Balanced growth and the avoidance of nutritional problems can best be achieved by paying attention to the ratios of the major nutrients in the substrate solution.

*Calcium deficiency* problems, for example, are less likely to develop, even in adverse climatic conditions, if the ratio of potassium to calcium is no higher than about 1.5 to 1 in the slabs. Since the slabs are more likely to accumulate calcium than potassium the feed ratio can usually go to 2 to 1 without risk.

Building the calcium level up too high, particularly in the presence of a lot of chloride, can lead to a problem with gold speck on the fruit. If the magnesium level is not kept up in proportion to calcium then *magnesium deficiency* symptoms will appear. The aim should be to keep a calcium to magnesium ratio in the slabs of around 5 to 1. The slight magnesium deficiency symptoms which often appear in the late spring cannot usually be avoided or corrected by supplying more magnesium to the substrate unless the level in the feed is below target. At the time of greatest risk, when the fruit load is building up to a maximum, there should be about 90 to 100 ppm of magnesium in the input solution if the conductivity is still around 3.5 to 4.0mS/cm.

*Phosphorus deficiency* is more likely to be caused by a high substrate pH locking up the nutrient in the slabs than by an inadequate supply in the feed. Some sources recommend 40 ppm of phosphorus either throughout the season or until first harvest, but even this may not be necessary with good pH control. Tomatoes seem able to take up enough phosphorus even when the substrate level falls below 10 ppm. It is important not to over-supply phosphorus because high up-take levels by the crop will induce *manganese deficiency,* which shows up as yellow chlorotic areas between the leaf veins. Magnesium uptake may be reduced too.

# 14 Cucumbers

*Propagation. Layout and preparation. Irrigation and nutrition.*

Cucumber seed can either be sown into small propagation cubes and moved into larger blocks after emergence, or sown directly into holes in the surface of 7.5 to 10cm square blocks. Common commercial practice is to germinate cucumber seeds in trays of vermiculite and prick off into growing blocks for new year/first crop plants, and to directly seed growing blocks for summer/second crop plants. The blocks should be spaced out as necessary to ensure that the leaves do not overlap at any stage. Germination should be carried out at a relatively low nutrient solution conductivity, around 1.5 mS/cm, but this should be raised gradually to the growing house conductivity (see below) as the plants increase in size.

## Grooved base blocks

Propagation blocks with grooved bases to aid drainage are ideal for cucumbers, as the plants are particularly susceptible to excess water in the substrate. The blocks should be placed with the grooves running in the same direction as the slope on the bench or glasshouse floor, and this orientation should be retained when the blocks are placed out on the slabs.

If grooved blocks are not used it is important that the blocks are placed on a layer of perlite or a similar granular material to prevent the blocks from sealing onto the polyethylene base sheet. The fine fibrous root system of cucumbers would seem to make them a less than ideal crop for slabs which have a relatively high water to air ratio, but with commercial yields of 150 cucumbers/sq m it is clear that they can cope well with any of the currently available materials, including low density slabs, if they are properly managed.

The temperature of the substrate during propagation should always be at least 20C and preferably a degree or two higher. Under-bench heating or heating pipe loops which are positioned to make maximum use of radiant heating directly into the slabs can be used to achieve this. The temperature of the applied irrigation water is also important at this stage because the volume which is put onto the blocks is large compared to their thermal volume. The water which is used for irrigation during the propagation period should either be heated to at least 18C or allowed to equilibrate to the glasshouse air temperature before it is applied to the crop.

## LAYOUT AND PREPARATION

Cucumbers are generally grown in standard rockwool slabs at a density of two plants per slab. The crop density in the growing house for a full-season crop is usually around 1.4 or 1.5 plants/sq m, allowing a substrate volume of at least 10 litres/sq m of glasshouse, and preferably a little more. Some cucumber production programmes are based on two or even three shorter crops each year, and in this case the density of the early crop or crops is usually 1.5 plants/sq m, with the autumn crop being put in at a lower density, around 1.2 plants/sq m to give better fruit quality as the growing conditions deteriorate.

Standard 7.5cm deep slabs are suitable, either 20 or 25cm wide, and either high or low density rockwool can be used depending on whether the slabs are to be re-used. A trial carried out in Holland several years ago demonstrated that 7.5cm deep slabs could produce the same long-season yields and quality as the 15cm deep slabs which were initially more popular with cucumber growers. In the same trial it was confirmed that the same crop performance could be achieved with either high density or low density rockwool. A comparison was also made between five sources of rockwool and two polyurethane foam slabs. All of the rockwool slabs gave similar results, and all out-performed the foam materials.

The most usual arrangement in the glasshouse is to use double rows of slabs with the plants spaced at between 40 and 50cm down each row. Alternatively the plants can be spaced at double density along a single row of slabs and trained in a V system. In this case the slabs should be placed touching in the row to avoid an excessive reduction in the volume of rockwool available for each plant.

Cucumbers respond well to root zone warming. If this is not available the heating pipes should be raised to slab height so that they can provide some radiant heat directly into the substrate. The optimum substrate temperature for cucumbers is around 21C to 23C.

## IRRIGATION

The slabs in the growing house should be allowed to warm up to at least 20C before the plants are stood on to them. This can be difficult to achieve in the case of an early crop unless root zone warming is available, and even with later plantings it is essential that the slabs are placed on to polystyrene slabs to prevent heat losses to the glasshouse floor. The slabs should be placed as close as possible to, but not touching, the heating pipes.

It is still important to use warm water for irrigation for the first week or two after planting while most of the root is still in the propagation blocks. The volume of water applied at this stage is small enough not to have a major effect on the temperature of the slabs, but cold water can still reduce the temperature of the small volume of substrate in the blocks dramatically. This problem is accentuated on sunny days when the heating pipes are cooler and the applied volume is greater. Under these conditions the root zone temperature can fall low enough to damage the root tips and allow a point of entry for fungal diseases like pythium.

The propagation blocks should be placed firmly on to the growing slabs, and the drip nozzles should be placed in position to irrigate through the blocks. Irrigation should at first be applied often enough to ensure that the slab volume below the blocks always remains wet enough to encourage root development downwards. Once the plants are well established the crop can be irrigated according to its water requirement.

On dull days the excess volume which is used to provide drainage should be limited to about 5% of the applied volume, and most of the crop demand should be applied during the early part of the day. In sunny conditions the drainage rate should be increased to at least 15 or 20%, and watering should extend through the day, with the last cycle about an hour before sunset.

If dull weather persists for several days there is a risk that the slab solution conductivity can rise too high, particularly from the accumulation of chlorides and sulphates. If this happens, the crop can be given a single increased volume application of nutrient solution early each day at a lower than normal conductivity to wash out the surplus salts.

## NUTRITION

Current feeding programmes for cucumbers recognise the need for substantial amounts of potassium during the cropping period, based on observations on a number of commercial crops. The ratio of potassium to calcium taken up by the crops was found to be close to 2 to 1 throughout the season, indicating that earlier recommendations for cucumbers on rockwool were under-supplying potassium during the harvesting period by as much as 40%. It is now recommended that the K to Ca ratio in the feed solution should be about 1.5 to 1 until about a week before the first fruits are cut, and then 2 to 1 for the rest of the season. A replanted summer crop should also be supplied at the higher calcium rate until just before first harvest.

### Conductivity and pH

The conductivity of the applied feed should be adjusted according to the time of year, the growing conditions and the stage of growth. The earliest crops, planted in northern Europe before the middle of January, need a feed conductivity of 3.0mS/cm until just before first pick, reducing to 2.8mS/cm while the stem fruit is being harvested, and then falling further to 2.0mS/cm for the rest of the year. Later plantings should start at 2.5mS/cm, reducing to 2.0mS/cm as the season progresses.

These values assume a relatively good quality water supply. If the water contains a significant amount of sodium all of these figures should be increased by about 0.3 to 0.5mS/cm.

Provided the slab solution conductivity does not increase much above 3.5mS/cm there is unlikely to be any loss of crop vigour, and experience in Holland indicates that by keeping the slab conductivity at around this level the fruit colour and quality can be better. In the UK most growers prefer to see summer slab levels no higher than about 2.5 to 3.0mS/cm, and this view has recently been supported by a trial in Canada which showed a worthwhile yield increase from relatively low summer conductivity levels, down to about 2.2mS/cm, without any significant reduction in fruit quality. An increase in slab conductivity to around 3.5 or 4.0mS/cm can be worthwhile towards the end of a late crop to improve fruit quality as growing conditions deteriorate.

The feed conductivity can be modified a little during harvesting to suit the vigour and balance of the crop. For example a late planting which is carrying a heavy fruit load on the primary stem will benefit from a higher strength feed with a more generous supply of potassium. It is particularly important with cucumbers to avoid a sudden reduction in the supply of potassium to the crop at any stage. If the crop has access to more potassium than it needs the uptake mechanism for this nutrient will be inhibited to prevent excessive amounts getting into the plants. A subsequent rapid reduction in the availability of potassium will then result in a period of potassium deficiency until the plants have been able to reverse the inhibition mechanism. Potassium deficiency in cucumbers is recognised by pale margins around the younger leaves leading in more severe cases to brown scorching of the leaf edges.

Cucumber crops are able to exert a considerable influence on the pH of the solution in the substrate. The target pH is between 5.5 and 6.0 in the root zone. During the winter when leaf growth is not adequately balanced by fruit development the crop tends to produce an increase in the pH of the substrate. This is because the roots of the plants are taking up a lot of nitrate and replacing it in the slab solution with bicarbonate, adding to the alkalinity buffering capacity of the solution. This can be prevented by keeping the feed solution pH down to 5.0, ensuring that the slabs are adequately flushed out, and if necessary adding a source of ammonium to the feed (see chapter 10).

### Nutrient sampling

With cucumbers it is particularly important to extract slab nutrient solution samples from within that part of the substrate which contains the active root system. There can sometimes be a big difference in the nutrient levels, the pH and the solution conductivity between the root zone and the unoccupied area of the slabs. This is caused by the rapid uptake of some nutrients, especially potassium, when the crop is carrying a lot of fruit.

A sample taken deep in the root zone at this stage will show a much lower conductivity than one taken close to the irrigation point. This should indicate the need for a period of stronger feeding, but this need will only be identified if samples are taken from within the root zone. Samples should therefore be taken from the slab mid-way between the plants rather than close to the irrigation points.

## Nutrient solutions for cucumbers

### Pre-harvest

| | | Conductivity (mS/cm) | | | |
|---|---|---|---|---|---|
| | | 1.5 | 2.0 | 2.5 | 3.0 |
| $NO_3$-N | (ppm) | 120 | 160 | 200 | 250 |
| $NH_4$-N | (ppm) | 7 | 7 | 7 | 7 |
| P | (ppm) | 30 | 30 | 30 | 30 |
| K | (ppm) | 180 | 230 | 300 | 375 |
| Ca | (ppm) | 120 | 155 | 200 | 250 |
| Mg | (ppm) | 25 | 35 | 45 | 55 |

*Micronutrients*

| | |
|---|---|
| Fe | 2.5 ppm |
| Cu | 0.1 ppm |
| Zn | 0.3 ppm |
| Mn | 0.5 ppm |
| B | 0.3 ppm |
| Mo | 0.1 ppm |

*These nutrient levels have a potassium to calcium ratio of 1.5 to 1*

### During harvesting

| | | Conductivity (mS/cm) | | |
|---|---|---|---|---|
| | | 2.0 | 2.5 | 2.8 |
| $NO_3$-N | (ppm) | 175 | 210 | 250 |
| $NH_4$-N | (ppm) | – | 7 | 7 |
| P | (ppm) | 35 | 35 | 40 |
| K | (ppm) | 280 | 340 | 400 |
| Ca | (ppm) | 140 | 170 | 200 |
| Mg | (ppm) | 40 | 45 | 55 |

*Micronutrients*

As for pre-harvest conditions

*These feeds have a potassium to calcium ratio of 2 to 1*

Unlike tomatoes, cucumbers do not respond well to high levels of sodium or chloride so neither of these materials should be used for conductivity control as they are for some other crops. The water source for cucumbers should contain no more than 50 ppm of sodium, and even at this level the build-up of salts, especially in a recirculating system, should be carefully monitored.

Cucumbers have a more specific requirement for an adequate supply of copper than most other crops. If the copper level in the substrate is too low there will be problems with the quality of the fruit, with both shape and colour deteriorating, and total yields will also be depressed. Cucumbers are also particularly sensitive to the levels of both boron and molybdenum, especially early in the year. Boron toxicity symptoms quickly appear if the slab boron levels are too high.

## The value of silicon

There is some evidence that cucumbers, like roses, benefit from the supply of the element silicon. Silicon is not normally thought of as an essential nutrient, but in the case of cucumbers it appears that an adequate supply of silicon in the substrate is required to improve the strength of the cell walls on the upper surface of the leaves. This in turn is supposed to improve resistance to the entry of fungal diseases such as mildew. The stronger, darker leaves that are produced when the crop is adequately supplied with silicon may also improve its photosynthetic ability, and therefore its yield potential.

There are trials results with cucumbers that seem to show that a yield increase of as much as 10% can be achieved by ensuring that the crop receives an adequate supply of silicon. In one experiment the incidence of powdery mildew was reduced from 35% to 21% by supplying silicon both in the nutrient solution and in the substrate.

Most soils and growing media contain more than enough silicon to meet the crop's needs, and in any case there is often enough silicon in the water supply. In an inert substrate there could be a problem if the water source contains less than the recommended 20 to 30 ppm of silicon. The most effective way of increasing the amount of silicon which is taken up by the crop is to add it to the nutrient solution in the form of potassium metasilicate. This material cannot be put into either of the main fertiliser stock solutions because it reacts chemically with the other fertilisers, so it has to be diluted from a third tank positioned downstream from the other two.

Other sources of silicon are available, but they are more difficult to keep in solution, so their use is more likely to result in nozzle blocking problems.

There is a further complication in that potassium metasilicate is strongly alkaline, so that when it is used a substantial increase in the amount of acid is also needed to neutralise the dilute nutrient solution. Potassium metasilicate also contains potassium, so the feed formulation has to be adjusted to take this extra supply into account. Liquid potassium metasilicate, containing 9% silicon, is used at a rate of up to 14 litres/1,000 litres of stock solution for dilution at 1 to 100, and at this rate it would require a reduction of 15kg in the amount of potassium nitrate in the feed and the addition of approximately 20 litres of 60% nitric acid, either added to the main stock solutions (not to the metasilicate stock solution) or supplied from the acid tank.

# 15 Other edible crops

*Peppers (capsicums). Melons. Climbing French beans. Aubergines. Lettuce. Strawberries.*

Nearly all of the sweet pepper crops produced under protection in northern Europe are now grown on substrates, the vast majority on rockwool. Peppers benefit greatly from root zone warming, and the ability to keep temperatures high in the substrate at a relatively low cost has been a major factor in the move out of the soil. Peppers are now firmly established as a high technology crop both in Holland and in the UK. Yields which are now taken for granted from full season crops would not have been considered possible a few years ago.

Plant propagation follows a similar programme to that described in chapter 13 for tomatoes. Seeds are sown individually either directly into large propagation blocks or into smaller cubes to be placed into the blocks after seedling emergence. Rockwool plugs can also be used for germination in a three-stage process, with the first move being into small cubes, then finally into 10cm blocks. The seed should be covered with a granulate material such as vermiculite to keep them moist until germination is complete. Alternatively the seeded cubes or plugs can be covered over with polyethylene film.

Seedlings which have been germinated in individual plugs or small cubes can be moved on to the next stage in batches to allow for the uneven germination rate which is common with this crop. The germination medium should be wetted with a pH adjusted water supply, but with little or no added nutrients. A high conductivity in the rockwool solution will greatly delay germination. For the same reason it is important that the medium is not allowed to dry out at all during the germination stage.

## Glasshouse layout and equipment

The layout of the glasshouse should follow the guidelines given for tomatoes except that in the case of peppers the provision of some form of substrate warming is essential for successful early production. The best option is to place the wrapped slabs onto rows of polystyrene slabs which carry warm water heating loops in grooves on their upper surface. If this is not practicable then the pipe loops for glasshouse heating should be positioned close to, but not touching, the slabs to provide as much radiant heat to the substrate as possible. The slabs should always be placed on to polystyrene to provide adequate thermal insulation from the glasshouse floor.

A thermal screen is also very useful for peppers. The need to establish rapid vegetative growth immediately after planting while running a high air temperature regime to minimise early fruit set means that the ability to maintain a humid atmosphere around the plants is a big advantage. Without a screen humidity levels early in the year can fall well below the 70-75% which is considered to be the minimum for avoiding plant stress. If a moveable screen is installed it can also be used in the summer for crop shading and humidity control.

A trial in Holland showed that the careful use of a screen during the summer, shading only when the crop was under maximum heat and light stress, increased both the yield and the quality of the fruit. If a fixed screen is used to minimise heat losses in the winter and to keep the humidity high it should be removed early in the spring before the crop shows any visible signs of soft weak growth.

## Training systems

Peppers grown on rockwool in top quality glass or in high light areas can be spaced to give a density as high as 7 stems/sq m, although 6 or even 5 stems will give better results in less ideal growing conditions. The number of plants needed per unit area to give this stem density depends on whether two or three stems are trained up from each plant. Taking three stems per plant gives some cost savings and can, with very good crop management, give equal or even higher yields than a two-stem crop. However in one trial in Holland a two-stem training system gave a 10% higher production over a full year compared to a three-stem system at the same shoot density. Most growers both in Europe and in North America take two stems per plant and aim for 5-6 stems/sq m of glasshouse by planting at a density of between 2.5 and 3 plants/sq m.

A V-training system is often used with a single row of rockwool slabs carrying plants which are trained up at an angle to form two rows. This has the advantage that fewer slabs are needed so the cost of the substrate is lower. It does, however, carry greater risks from the smaller volume of substrate which is available to each plant, particularly if the irrigation system is less than perfect. In this case it is worth considering a compromise by using a wider slab. There will still be some cost savings, but the safety margin is greater.

For V-trained crops the rockwool slabs should in any case be placed at maximum density in the row with no gaps between adjacent slabs.

It is particularly important with early planted pepper crops to get the crop off to a good start. It is necessary to develop the vegetative framework of the crop adequately before allowing the crop to switch into fruit production. Even in the ideal growing conditions which can be provided by substrate growing, a crop which is allowed to build up a substantial fruit load too early will suffer an extended period of low production before balance can be restored. This comes at a time when market values are still high so the net loss of yield is translated into an even greater loss of income.

## Growing conditions

The plants will be ready to go into rockwool slabs six to nine weeks after sowing, depending on the growing conditions. As soon as the plants have been placed on to the slabs in the growing house they should be provided with a mean air temperature of 21-22C, with day temperatures a little higher than night temperatures. The substrate temperature should be maintained at a similar level.

Temperatures as high as this will prevent most flowers from setting, but any fruits which succeed in developing, particularly the crown fruit in the lowest axil, should be removed by hand to keep the plants growing. Even fruit left at the second axil level should also be completely removed from early crops, leaving a clear height of about 40cm above the slab. The small increase in early yield which they would generate would be more than offset by greater losses in production a few weeks later. In any case, fruit which is allowed to form in the first or second axils is often deformed as the plant is not at this stage open enough to give space for unrestricted fruit development.

The ideal growing conditions provided in a heated substrate make it possible to allow fruit development to begin at an earlier stage than would be safe for a soil-grown crop. Exactly when to do this has to be left to the grower's judgement. A decision has to be made on the basis of the total leaf area of the crop and the extent to which the roots have penetrated the slabs. When this stage is reached the night temperature is gradually reduced over a period of one to two weeks to 17 or 18C and the crop will respond by producing larger flowers which set much more readily.

### Nutrient management

The general nutritional guidelines given in chapter 13 for tomatoes can for the most part be used for peppers. There are, however, one or two important differences, relating specifically to early crop vigour and to avoiding blossom end rot. Unlike tomatoes, where the most important objective after planting is to restrict excessive vegetative growth and encourage fruit setting, with peppers it is necessary to encourage as much early plant growth as possible. This means that the early season conductivity targets are different. A suitable feed for an open system during the main growing season (see panel) has a conductivity of about 2.5mS/cm, and this is intended to produce slab conductivity levels of around 3.0 to 3.5mS/cm. The same targets should be used in a recirculating system.

Excessively low slab conductivities, while they will encourage maximum plant growth, can at the same time cause an increase in the incidence of silver flecking of the fruit surface. The minimum slab conductivity at any time should therefore be about 2.7mS/cm. During propagation and to wet up the growing slabs a feed conductivity of no more than 3.0mS/cm should be used unless the light levels reaching the crop are consistently low, such as under a fixed screen, when up to 4.0mS/cm can be considered safe.

Blossom end rot is by far the most common physiological disorder of peppers. It can appear suddenly and extensively, often with disastrous financial consequences. It is caused by the inability of the plants to take up enough calcium and to move it into the developing fruits. Blossom end rot can develop at any time but it is particularly common when the crop is carrying a heavy fruit load early in the summer, especially if environmental factors like high temperatures and low humidities are causing stress on the plants. Maintaining an even fruit load – which is by no means easy – and avoiding stress factors will help to reduce the effects of blossom end rot, but careful nutrition management can also play a major part.

A high conductivity in the slab solution increases the risk of blossom end rot and increases its severity when

### Nutrient solution for peppers

| | |
|---|---|
| $NH_4$-N | 18 ppm |
| $NO_3$-N | 215 ppm |
| P | 46 ppm |
| K | 250 ppm |
| Ca | 200 ppm |
| Mg | 45 ppm |

*Micronutrients*

| | |
|---|---|
| Fe | 0.55 ppm |
| Cu | 0.50 ppm |
| Zn | 0.35 ppm |
| Mn | 0.55 ppm |
| B | 0.35 ppm |
| M | 0.07 ppm |

*These recommendations, which are for an open system, replace earlier recommendations which had higher potassium levels and lower calcium levels. For a recirculation system the levels of the major nutrients should be reduced to about 75 to 80% of those given above. The sodium level should be below 140 ppm and the chloride should be below 200 ppm.*

it is already present. This is because the root system's ability to take up calcium from the nutrient solution is reduced when the total conductivity is high, irrespective of the amount of calcium which is present in the solution.

When a heavy fruit load is developing it is important to ensure that the substrate solution conductivity stays on target by irrigating more heavily or by reducing the input solution conductivity slightly.

## K to Ca ratio

The make-up of the feed has also proved to be important in avoiding blossom end rot. Recent changes in the standard Dutch recommendations for feeding peppers in rockwool have focussed on the need to maintain a lower K to Ca ratio in the slabs.

The aim should be to produce a ratio of K to Ca in the slabs of no more than 0.75. For example with a potassium level of 180 ppm the calcium level should be at least 240 ppm. Some sources are now advising even more extreme K to Ca ratios, sometimes as low as 0.5, during periods of greatest risk but these need to be carefully monitored to make sure that potassium deficiency is not allowed to develop. A ratio of 0.5 can mean a potassium level as low as 100 to 120 ppm in the slabs. This is not a problem if it is maintained at this level but if there is a sudden increase in the crop demand for potassium the level in the slabs can fall to 60 ppm or below, and this can result in the marginal chlorosis which is typical of potassium deficiency.

Experimental evidence from Holland has confirmed the importance of a low K to Ca ratio in the slab solution, with the lowest percentage of blossom end rot resulting from ratios of 0.5 or below. It is important to note that the quoted ratios are for the nutrient levels in the slabs rather than in the input solution. Calcium generally builds up in the slabs and potassium is depleted, so an input ratio of 1.25 K to Ca is likely to produce a slab ratio of around 0.75. Excessively high calcium levels can cause a physiological disorder, with excess calcium in the fruit appearing as small dark pits on the surface.

Magnesium deficiency in the foliage is a further risk, and the magnesium level in the slabs should always be balanced to that of calcium, with a typical target of 70 to 75 ppm.

## Sodium sensitivity

Peppers are sensitive to the level of sodium in the slab solution and this can be a problem in recirculating systems if the water supply or any of the fertilisers contain significant amounts of sodium. A trial carried out at Naaldwijk in Holland showed that high sodium levels will reduce the crop yield by decreasing the size of the fruit. The problem is greater if the circulating nutrient solution also contains a lot of calcium.

There seems to be a positive link with potassium supply and it may be that if the ratio of potassium to sodium is maintained by increasing the potassium level in proportion to the increase in sodium, sodium's adverse effect on yield could be reduced or eliminated. However there is then the risk that the higher potassium levels could increase the incidence of blossom end rot.

## MELONS

Melons are not yet widely grown on rockwool but their fragile root system and sensitivity to root temperature make them ideal candidates for substrate growing. Like cucumbers they need a relatively high air supply to the roots, so it is important that the structure of the slab is such that the air content is adequate even immediately after irrigation. Trials have shown that vertical fibre orientation is preferable to horizontal fibre slabs for melons, and that free drainage at the base of the slabs, if possible accompanied by a slope across the width of the slab, gives the best growing conditions for this crop. For the same reason single season low density rockwool slabs have sometimes given poor results with melons.

The growth of melons on rockwool is quite different to that of soil-grown crops. The plants tend to flower more freely and to set more fruit so that more, but smaller, fruit are produced. For this reason the choice of variety is important. It is better to use a variety which normally produces a small number of relatively large fruit when grown in the soil, such as Galia. Ogen types grown in rockwool produce many fruit, but the fruit size is often not up to market requirements.

The layout of the glasshouse and the general culture of melons is very similar to that described for cucumbers in chapter 14. There was at one time a trend towards using a larger slab for melons, sometimes 20cm wide by 10cm deep, but more experience with the crop and better irrigation management has in most cases made this unnecessary. Generally a 20/75 (4 plant) or 15/75 size slab (2–3 plants) is used. Slabs can be reused two or three times. Melons are much more sensitive than cucumbers to low root and air temperatures. As with cucumbers, substrate warming early in the year gives substantial benefits and early production should not be considered unless this facility is available. A slab temperature as high as 25C gives excellent results, and an air temperature as low as 18 to 20C can be used in conjunction with this to give some good overall fuel savings.

Propagation of melon plants for use on rockwool is done in the same way as for cucumbers, germinating the seed in small individual cubes which are then moved into larger blocks before the final move on to the slabs.

The quick establishment of melons into the ideal growing conditions of the slabs can be a disadvantage in terms of early fruit set. The crop can become excessively vigorous and this can result in a delay in flowering so that the first fruits are carried too high up on the plants. This problem can be minimised by holding the plants a bit longer in the propagation blocks before allowing them to root into the slabs. The extent to which this can be safely done depends on the accuracy of the irrigation system and the quality of crop management. Any drying out at the roots at this stage will cause long-term problems. An alternative is to plant in the normal way and then raise the EC when flowers appear until fruit set to control plant vigour (EC 3.0–3.5mS/cm).

## Flavour factors

Some work on the potassium requirements of melons was recently carried out in Italy. The flavour of melons in rockwool and other substrates is sometimes disappointing, with quite low sugar contents being recorded. Attempts were made to produce higher quality fruit by using a feeding regime which supplied increasing amounts of potassium to the crop as the fruit approached harvest, up to a maximum of 660 ppm.

This approach did not prove to be very successful, and neither was an alternative approach, based on increasing the slab conductivity in stages up to a maximum of 4.4mS/cm.

It seems that any improvements which can be made in the sugar content of melons by manipulating the nutrition is masked by the greater natural variation in sugar content between cultivars and between individual plants of the same cultivar.

### Crop management

Melons in rockwool are fed in a similar way to cucumbers. The conductivity of the input solution at the start of the crop should be 2.0 to 2.5mS/cm. A conductivity of around 2.5mS/cm is suitable throughout the life of the crop although some growers have had equally good results with conductivities as high as 3.5mS/cm or as low as 1.8mS/cm.

The most important rule is to maintain a consistent conductivity within the slabs except when a change in the balance of the crop is needed. An over-vigorous crop with inadequate fruit setting can be improved by a moderate rise in the slab conductivity for a week or two, while a fruit-laden crop can be encouraged back into vegetative growth by weaker feeding. In the absence of any firm evidence for the precise nutritional requirements of melons it is usual to use a nutrient solution similar to that used for cucumbers (see chapter 14).

The irrigation requirements for melons are different to those for cucumbers because the maximum water uptake by melons in the summer is a lot lower. The maximum requirement is of the order of no more than 4 litres/plant/day at peak demand. Because of the need to maintain good aeration in the root zone frequent applications of relatively small volumes of water may be the best option, but it is important to keep enough nutrient solution passing through the slabs to avoid any build up of sodium, to which melons are particularly sensitive. To avoid salt build-up in the summer, night watering may be advisable.

## CLIMBING FRENCH BEANS

Flat podded climbing french beans are grown in rockwool on a small scale in Holland, the extra costs being recovered in higher production and more uniform crop growth. Substrate warming is needed for the earliest sowing but most growers prefer a March planting, for which warm air heating is adequate. In this case substrate heating is not used but it is important to place the rockwool slabs on to polystyrene to insulate them from the glasshouse floor.

Two crops per year are achieved, with a mid to late March planting cropping between early May and the middle of July, followed by a July planting for autumn production. The harvesting period for each crop lasts five to seven weeks and the bulk of the production comes from the spring crop.

There is so far no consensus of opinion in Holland as to the best glasshouse layout for beans, and trials are still under way to sort this out. The two front-runners are to plant either two or four rows per 3.2m glasshouse bay using a plant spacing of 60cm or 30cm in the row respectively, in each case giving an overall plant density of a little over 2 plants/sq m. The most recent trials evidence points to the two row system giving marginally better quality, especially in the autumn. This option also appears to be quicker to harvest, as the developing beans are more visible. Closer spacings than 2 plants/sq m have been tried, but the gain in yield is generally offset by a higher proportion of misshapen beans.

Propagation of beans is usually done in 10cm rockwool blocks, sowing two seeds per block so that each block contains two plants when it is put on to the slab. A nutrient solution with a conductivity of around 2.5 or 3.0mS/cm is used from propagation to the end of the crop. The basic cucumber feed is suitable for beans but there is some evidence that rather higher magnesium levels are better for beans, which are particularly sensitive to magnesium deficiency.

Beans are less tolerant than most crops to a low pH, picking up too much manganese in particular and quickly exhibiting the interveinal leaf bronzing symptoms which are characteristic of manganese toxicity. It is usual to adjust the pH of the feed solution to give a slab pH around 6.0 for beans crop to prevent manganese toxicity. Reducing the amount of manganese in the input solution will not prevent manganese toxicity from developing if the pH falls too low.

Because of the susceptibility of this crop to low substrate pH it is better not to include any ammonium nitrate in the feed.

## AUBERGINES

Aubergines are quite widely grown in rockwool, following trials carried out in the 1980's which indicated substantial yield increases from the use of substrates. The relatively coarse and deep root system of this crop led initially to the use of deep slabs, 10cm or more, but most growers now use the standard 7.5cm deep slabs without problems. The layout of the cropping house follows that used for cucumbers, while plant propagation techniques are generally the same as those described for peppers. There is no direct evidence for the benefits of substrate warming for aubergines, but in view of the high temperature requirements for early production it is likely that substrate warming would be economically justified in northern Europe.

Seed is sown in small cubes or multiblocks of rockwool, and the seedlings are later moved into larger progagation blocks which are eventually placed out on to the rockwool slabs. A typical plant spacing is around 2.5 plants/sq m if two shoots are taken from each plant, but no more than 2 plants/sq m for a three-shoot training system. If the shoot density is too high it becomes very diffi-cult to manage the crop effectively and pest and disease control also becomes more difficult.

Vegetative development should be encouraged at first by maintaining a high night temperature, and no fruit should be allowed to develop on the plants until a strong framework has been built up. The standard cucumber feed is suitable for aubergines. Research in Jersey suggests that an initial conductivity around 3.0mS/cm may be worthwhile to prevent too much vigour until fruit is allowed to set, but subsequently the conductivity in the slabs should as far as possible be kept down to 2.0mS/cm because it is difficult to maintain the vigour of the crop when it is carrying a heavy load of fruit.

As with beans, there is some evidence that aubergines will benefit from relatively high levels of magnesium, with a compensating reduction in potassium and calcium to keep the total conductiv-ity down.

## LETTUCE

Lettuce is not widely grown through to harvest on rockwool, nutrient fim technique (NFT) being preferred by many of the major producers. The use of rockwool for propagation and establishment into the NFT troughs gives excellent results however. Either pelleted or bare seed can be used, the former lending itself to mechanised sowing methods. Propagation cubes approximately 2.5cm square and 4cm deep are generally used, wetted up with a nutrient solution of conductivity 1.5mS/cm before sowing. It is not necessary to cover the seeds, especially if they are pelleted, but it is important to maintain the moisture level of the rockwool throughout the propagation stage.

The cubes containing seedlings are placed into specially designed NFT troughs, and supplied with a continuous flow of nutrient solution in a thin film to allow adequate aeration. A typical recirculating solution for NFT lettuce has a conductivi-ty of about 2.3mS/cm, and the nutrient levels shown in the panel.

The residual nitrate nitrogen content of the leaves at harvest is an important factor in the production of lettuce and other leaf salad vegetables. Many countries now set upper limits on nitrate levels, and these are often difficult to meet when a crop is grown in the soil, particularly in the winter months.

Using an inert substrate makes it possible to manipulate the nutrition of the crop to minimise the nitrate content at harvest. Research in Holland investigated various techniques which

| Nutrient solution for lettuce in NFT/rockwool | |
|---|---|
| $NO_3$-N | 200 ppm |
| P | 60 ppm |
| K | 300 ppm |
| Ca | 170 ppm |
| Mg | 50 ppm |
| | |
| Fe | 3.0 ppm |
| Cu | 0.1 ppm |
| Zn | 0.1 ppm |
| Mn | 2.0 ppm |
| B | 0.3 ppm |
| Mo | 0.2 ppm |

could be used to reduce the residual nitrate level in lettuce at the end of the crop. It was found that removing nitrogen from the nutrient solution shortly before harvest was effective, but that it often resulted in tipburn.

Using a new nitrogenous fertiliser, calcium proteinate, in combination with ammonium chloride and ammonium nitrate, proved to be more successful. An additional reduction in residual nitrate can then be achieved by gradually increasing the chloride content at the expense of nitrate towards the end of the crop without any risk of tipburn.

## STRAWBERRIES

Rockwool is being increasingly used for strawberries grown under protection. Short day varieties are used to give an early harvest before the outdoor crop is ready, and to follow on with a second harvest once the bulk of the outdoor production is finished. The time of flowering, and therefore of harvest, is controlled by providing the rooted runners with a period of chilling in a cold store.

Standard 7.5cm deep wrapped slabs are normally used, but some growers prefer the extra volume of substrate provided by 10cm deep slabs. The slabs are often set on to benches to make picking easier. The length and width of the slabs is chosen to suit the layout of the glasshouse, and 20cm or wider slabs are most commonly used. It is not usually practical to provide one irrigation drip per plant, but at least three per slab should be used, distributed over the surface to give an even supply of nutrient solution throughout the slab volume.

The slabs should be wetted up before use with a nutrient solution with a conductivity around 1.5 to 2.0mS/cm, after which the drainage slits are cut at the base of the slabs prior to planting. A tomato feed is generally used both to wet up the slabs and to grow the crop as little work has been done on the specific nutrient requirements of strawberries in rockwool. It is likely, though, that the potassium demand increases as the fruit is swelling so the feed should be adjusted at this stage to take account of this.

The plants should be put into the rockwool when the temperature of the solution used to wet them up has had time to equilibrate with the air temperature in the glasshouse. Bare root plants can be used, and these are set into planting holes cut into the top of the rockwool slab. Alternatively the plants can be rooted into rockwool blocks, which are then set on to the surface of the slab as usual.

*Various types of drip irrigation nozzle suit rockwhool substrates. The most important characteristics are the uniformity of delivery and resistance to blockages*

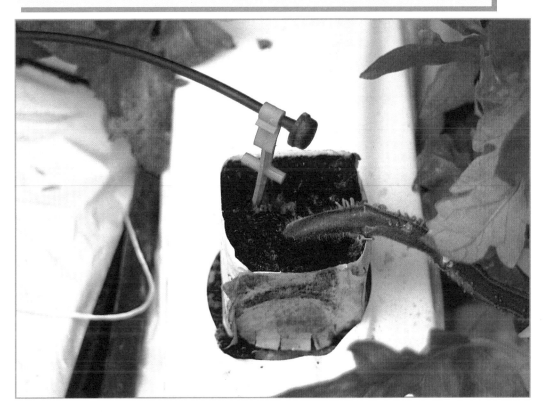

Irrigation is usually managed by computer which triggers irrigation cycles to a number of glasshouse compartments in turn. Signals from the controller (left) open and close solenoid vales on the flow and return lines to each area (below). Pressure monitors in the line (bottom) passes information back to the computer; if pressure is too low the computer signals a supply failure, if too high an unacceptable level of nozzle blockages

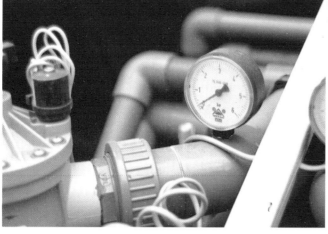

Opposite: A typical stock solution preparation area. Fertilisers are pre-dissolved in the black tank (left foreground) so that only fully dissolved materials reach the white stock tanks. After fertiliser injection, the dilute solution is mixed and monitored for pH and cf in the round tank (right foreground) before being pumped to the crop
[Picture courtesy Ballakinnish Nurseries Ltd, Isle of Man]

An alternative layout for a stock solution preparation area (above). Here fertilisers are not pre-dissolved, but a motor-driven mixer blade in each tank ensures that the fertilisers are fully dissolved. The mixing tank (left foreground) has pH and cf monitors set into its lid to check the accuracy of dilution before the nutrient solution reaches the crop

Simple injectors (left) work on a fixed ratio between stock solution and water supply usually 1:100. More sophisitcated systems allow the ratio to be varied to achieve any set conductivity level. Simple hand-held conductivity and pH meters (above) are a must for checking on the performance of the fertiliser injection system and on the conditions in the substrate

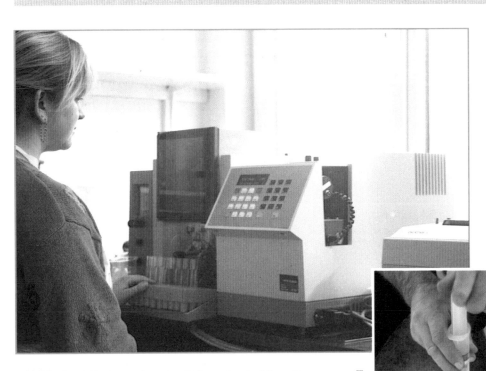

Nutrient solution samples should be extracted from the substrate (right) and sent to a horticultural laboratory for full chemical analysis (above). Occasionally leaf samples are taken for plant sap analysis (below). This adds to the grower's understanding of how his substrate-grown crop is performing

It is important to dissolve fertilisers in the correct volume of water. Marking each tank with a scale (left) makes this easier

In the Netherlands it is possible to buy fertilisers pre-dissolved as liquid concentrates. These are delivered individually to the nursery (below), stored in separate tanks (bottom) and used in appropriate proportions to make up stock solutions

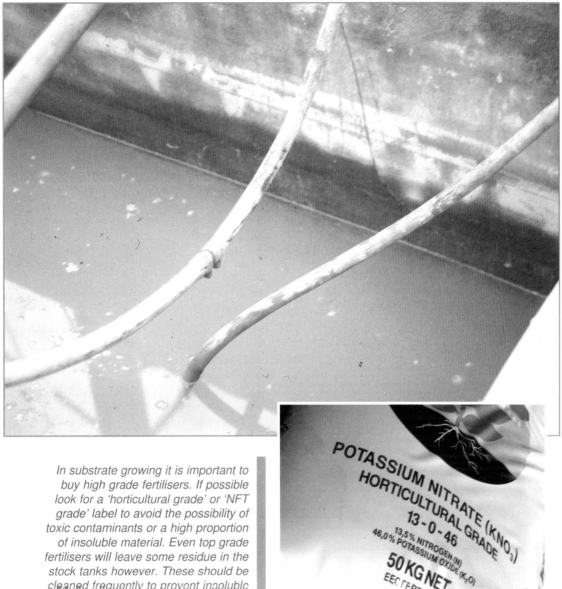

In substrate growing it is important to buy high grade fertilisers. If possible look for a 'horticultural grade' or 'NFT grade' label to avoid the possibility of toxic contaminants or a high proportion of insoluble material. Even top grade fertilisers will leave some residue in the stock tanks however. These should be cleaned frequently to prevent insoluble material from passing into the irrigation system. The take-off pipe should be raised above the base of the tank for the same reason

Propagating into pre-formed rockwool cubes (above)

Cut flower crops like gerberas (below) and lisianthus (right) adapt well to substrate growing. Gerberas are commonly grown off the ground to keep the substrate temperature as high as possible, particularly in winter. This also makes it easier and quicker to harvest the blooms

[Pictures courtesy Grodania A/S & Rockwool Grodan BV]

# 16 Roses

*Propagation. Layout and preparation. Planting and establishment. Irrigation and nutrition. Crop disorders.*

Roses were first produced commercially in rockwool more than 20 years ago in Denmark, with the Dutch starting to take up the idea a couple of years later. Despite the success of the technique growers in Holland were surprisingly slow to follow it up, and most of the expansion of the Dutch rose industry into rockwool has occurred in the last few years. There is a natural hesitation to believe that a deep rooted crop like roses can be reliably managed in a few centimeters depth of substrate, particularly when the material has to remain in good condition for the five to seven years that a commercial rose crop will be kept in production.

Despite these misgivings, roses continue to produce excellent long-term crops in rockwool and few growers now have any reservations about using it. One of the first benefits which rose growers find when switching to rockwool is the speed of establishment of the new crop and the correspondingly short interval between planting and first harvest. Worthwhile production from a rockwool rose crop can start within three months after planting compared to six months or more for a soil-grown crop. This advantage is maintained in subsequent years, with the optimum growing conditions which can be applied to a rockwool crop ensuring top yields and quality throughout the life of the crop.

The yield advantages are not always great, and it may be that a well grown rockwool crop will not produce more stems over its lifetime than a similar crop grown in a well-structured clean soil. Compared to a crop grown in less than perfect soil conditions, on the other hand, the improvement is often spectacular.

## PLANT PROPAGATION

One by-product of the move into rockwool was the realisation that many varieties perform as well or better on their own roots than when they are grafted on to a rootstock. This led the way to the development of the simplified plant propagation technique based on rooting stem cuttings which is now widely used.

There are exceptions to this, as some long stemmed varieties only produce top quality plants when they are grafted. The form of grafting most commonly used for modern rose varieties is known as mini-splicing, in which a leafy scion of the flowering variety is grafted on to an aerial shoot of the rootstock variety.

*Whichever propagation method is used, growers should be aware that if they intend to take propagation material from their own flowering stocks of modern cultivars they will probably be liable to pay plant breeders' royalties.*

## Taking cuttings

Single node cuttings are usually used for own-root plant production, each carrying one five-leaflet leaf, taken from the middle of semi-mature stems on healthy plants. It is not usual to select plants for use as mother stocks on the basis of their cropping performance, but there is no reason why this should not be done if the aim is to generate an improvement in either the yield or the bloom quality.

It is not necessary to use only flowering stems as propagation material. It has been shown that cuttings taken from blind shoots will perform just as well as those taken from flowering shoots. Research in Denmark has demonstrated that varieties like Frisco and Gabrielle can actually yield up to 10% *higher* from cuttings taken from blind wood rather than from flowering shoots. There is no evidence that cuttings taken from blind wood will themselves produce any more blind shoots than cuttings taken from flowering shoots.

It is best to reject cuttings with damaged leaves as it has been shown that these root more slowly. Large cuttings can be trimmed back cleanly to four or even two leaflets, however, without affecting their rooting ability. Each cutting is then trimmed to just above and about 4cm below the eye and the base is dipped into a rooting hormone such as 0.5% IBA powder or solution. Experience with specific varieties may indicate that a higher or lower hormone concentration is more effective in some circumstances.

The cuttings are then stuck to a depth of 1 to 2cm, either into small propagation cubes or into larger blocks about 7 to 8cm square. These should be wetted with a pH-adjusted nutrient solution with a conductivity of around 1.0mS/cm. If the water quality is poor it is possible to use a slightly higher conductivity to ensure some nutrient content, but this should be no higher than 1.5mS/cm otherwise the growth of the new shoots may be impeded. The blocks should be well drained from the base either by using a grooved block or by standing flat-based blocks on a thin layer of perlite on top of a polyethylene sheet on a flat surface.

## Rooting

The cuttings are most easily rooted under tents with the help of mist, using under-bench heating if necessary to achieve a minimum substrate temperature of 18C. The air temperature should be in the range 19 to 21C throughout the propagation period. The cuttings should be shaded from strong sun, but they otherwise need to receive as much light as possible so the tent should be covered with perforated clear polyethylene rather than white or coloured plastic. Irrigation with a low strength nutrient solution should be applied as often as necessary to keep the blocks moist. If the misting system applies enough volume to keep the blocks wet they should still be flushed through occasionally with a weak nutrient solution to make sure that the cuttings are always adequately supplied with nutrients.

Supplementary lighting at an intensity of about 40 to 50W/sq m – equivalent to about 4,000 to 5,000 lux – can be used to good effect in the winter to extend the daylength to 12 or 14 hours. With supplementary lighting or in good natural light conditions the cuttings should have produced roots visible on the base of the blocks within two to four weeks. The young plants should be hardened off before they are stood out on to the growing slabs, which should not be unnecessarily delayed otherwise the roots can be damaged and phytophthora can become established. Planting is usually done within about six weeks after striking, by which time the developing shoots will have reached a height of 30 to 40cm.

## Planting

When the plants have been placed on to the slabs it is usual to encourage maximum side shoot production by bending or breaking the first shoot above the basal root initials. The alternative is to let them come up to flowering and then to remove the opening flower. These operations can be continued for up to two months to develop as much photosynthetic area on the crop as possible before the first flush is taken. Bloom quality will then be much better, particularly during the winter under northern European conditions.

## LAYOUT AND PREPARATION

Since a commercial rose crop will remain in place for several years it is important that the preparation of the glasshouse is thorough and that the layout of the rockwool installation is appropriate. Most rockwool rose crops are now grown in closed systems, either with or without recirculation, and this trend will continue in the future as the protection of the environment becomes a more urgent issue in most horticultural areas. Even if there is no requirement to isolate the growing system at planting time the situation could be quite different six or seven years later, so it makes sense to at least build in the facility to contain and collect the drainage from the system.

The glasshouse should be accurately levelled and profiled before the rockwool installation is put into place, with the path areas fully covered with UV-stabilised polyethylene sheets at least 0.1mm thick. These will have to provide an effective barrier between the crop and the soil for several years so thinner material is not adequate.

The drip irrigation system for roses must be capable of providing 1 litre/hour/nozzle, and there should preferably be at least six nozzles per growing slab. It is even better if one nozzle per plant can be provided, as they can then be put directly into each propagation block. If the nozzle density is significantly less than six per slab then the flow rate should be increased in proportion.

Roses are grown on slabs, usually standard sized 20cm wide and 7.5cm deep although some growers prefer the greater security of 10cm deep slabs, which are in any case better for the most vigorous varieties. Some crop layouts are geared to 30cm or even 45cm wide slabs. If it is not possible to provide one nozzle per plant it is better to use these wider slabs to ensure an adequate water supply throughout each slab. If there is a slope across the width of the slab and the nozzles are not put directly into the propagation blocks they should be offset towards the 'top' edge of the slab to get the best distribution of nutrient solution within the slab.

Wrapped slabs are usually used but unwrapped slabs are suitable if they are separately covered with polyethylene sheet after they have been placed in position.

Whether the slabs are placed directly on to a profiled, covered glasshouse floor or put into troughs they should be put on to polystyrene slabs.

Heating loops set into the upper surface are worth considering as roses have been shown to respond well to substrate warming. For a profiled installation it is usual to provide a gradient across the slabs of 2 to 3% to allow drainage to run away from the path and into the gap between adjacent rows of slabs. Accurate profiling and careful positioning of the slabs are important because up to 40% over-watering may be needed at times to maintain an optimum nutrient status and it is essential that this extra volume is quickly and effectively removed from the slabs.

## PLANTING AND ESTABLISHMENT

The growing slabs must be thoroughly wetted before the crop is put into place. A standard nutrient solution with a conductivity of about 1.5 to 2.0mS/cm is used for this purpose. The higher end of the range should be used if there is a significant salt content in the water supply. Wrapped slabs are wetted by positioning the irrigation nozzles to feed through the planting holes and applying at least 12 litres of nutrient solution per standard size slab.

Drainage slits should be cut diagonally down to floor level along the lower edge of the slabs, usually two or three per slab, but this operation should be delayed for a week or so to ensure that the full volume of rockwool is saturated.

Unwrapped slabs are more of a problem, and these have to be wetted by hand before they are covered, using a hose to which is attached a coarse sprinkler.

The slab temperature should be allowed to equilibrate to about 18 to 20C before planting.

### Crop density

The standard crop density under average northern European growing conditions is around 6 to 8 plants/sq m of glasshouse depending on the variety. The way this density is achieved depends on the layout of the glasshouse and the slab width. Two rows of plants can be put on to a 20cm wide slab, although some growers put a single row at closer spacing. The irrigation nozzles are put directly on to the propagation blocks if there are enough of them, otherwise they are set along the outside edge of the slab.

In areas of very high light intensities such as the south west United States or in Mediterranean countries a lower plant density, perhaps as low as 4 or 5 plants/sq m, has been shown to give similar or even better results to those which can be achieved at traditional plant densities. Conversely, in poor light areas the density can be taken up to 12 plants/sq m to make maximum use of the available space, especially when the crop is carried on mobile benches. This carries greater risks in terms of disease management and control, but it is generally thought that this is justified by the higher yields.

Own-root cuttings establish quickly when the blocks are placed out on to the growing slabs. Frequent small waterings are needed during the first few days after the blocks are stood out on the slabs. This keeps the root system which is contained within the blocks adequately supplied with water until the plants have made enough depth of root to find the water table in the growing slabs. The volume of available water in each propagation block is small compared to the requirements of the plants at this stage and there is a risk that any drying out, which will be accompanied by an increase in the concentration of the nutrient solution, could damage the developing roots and delay the establishment of the crop. The frequency of irrigation is then gradually reduced, and the volume increased, as the crop becomes fully established into the slabs.

## IRRIGATION AND NUTRITION

It has been shown that about 96% of the water up-take by a rose crop takes place during the day and the remaining 4% at night so the irrigation regime can be set to take this pattern into account. A single irrigation cycle is often applied at night to make sure that the irrigation lines are not left for too long a period without flushing through. The up-take of nutrients by the crop follows a slightly different pattern, with 16% of uptake occurring at night. In other words the plants are taking up a stronger solution at night than during the day and there is likely to be a gradual fall in the slab conductivity between the evening and the following morning.

Generous irrigation rates to keep the slab solution conductivity close to that of the input solution have always given the best results with roses. In one French trial a 40% drainage rate accompanied by the lowest of three experimental slab conductivities gave the best results in terms of crop yield, stem length and flower weight. Keeping the glasshouse humidity above 70% during the day with high pressure misting units proved to be beneficial, too, but this work was carried out in the south of France where daytime humidity levels can fall a lot lower than in northern Europe.

The nutritional requirements of roses in rockwool have been gradually refined over the last decade, with the result that a standard feed formulation has been established.

These levels are not universally adopted – some sources, for example, advise more nitrogen, lower levels of phosphorus, potassium and calcium, and different ratios of micronutrients. Roses do not seem to have any particularly unusual nutritional requirements except that they are inclined to take up excessive amounts of manganese at the expense of iron if they are given the opportunity, so it is best to keep the Fe to Mn ratio at 4 or above in the slabs at all times to avoid iron deficiency symptoms. This problem is more likely to develop if the pH is low, so the pH of the slab solution should be frequently checked.

**Standard nutrient solution for roses in rockwool**

| | |
|---|---|
| $NH_4$-N | 10 ppm |
| $NO_3$-N | 180 ppm |
| P | 50 ppm |
| K | 235 ppm |
| Ca | 180 ppm |
| Mg | 24 ppm |
| | |
| Fe | 1.40 ppm |
| Cu | 0.05 ppm |
| Zn | 0.23 ppm |
| Mn | 0.28 ppm |
| B | 0.22 ppm |
| Mo | 0.05 ppm |

### The benefit of silicon

Unlike most crops, but in common with cucumbers (p98), roses appear to benefit from the supply of silicon. Silicon is not usually included in lists of essential nutrients but in the case of these crops it seems that silicon is needed to strengthen the cell walls, particularly those of the upper leaf surface. This appears to improve the crop's resistance to fungal diseases such as mildew. Experimental evidence suggests that with roses yield increases of as much as 10% can be achieved by ensuring an adequate supply of silicon to the crop. This may be brought about either indirectly from the improved mildew resistance, or directly from the increase in photosynthetic leaf area which sometimes appears to accompany silicon enrichment.

Fortunately most soils and organic growing media contain more than enough silicon to meet the needs of the crop, and where this is not the case there is often enough silicon in the water supply. In an inert substrate like rockwool, though, there could be problems if the water source contains less than the recommended 20 ppm of silicon. Silicon can be added to the nutrient solution under these circumstances but this is unfortunately not a simple matter. The most suitable soluble form of silicon for application in solution is potassium metasilicate, but this material cannot be put into either of the main fertiliser stock solutions because it reacts chemically with the other fertilisers. It therefore has to be diluted from a third tank, positioned below the other two.

There is a further complication in that potassium metasilicate is strongly alkaline so that when it is used a substantial increase in the amount of acid is also needed to neutralise the dilute nutrient solution. Potassium metasilicate also contains potassium, so the feed formualtion has to be adjusted to take this extra supply into account. Liquid potassium metasilicate, containing 9% silicon, is used at a rate of up to 14 litres/1,000 litres of stock solution for dilution at 1 to100, and at this rate it would require a reduction of 15kg in the amount of potassium nitrate in the feed and the addition of approximately 20 litres of 60% nitric acid.

## pH and conductivity

A few years ago roses in rockwool were always fed at a low conductivity, around 1.5mS/cm, but it has become clear recently that they will perform equally well at conductivities of between 2.0 and 3.0mS/cm. At these levels there is more scope for adjusting the nutrient balance, particularly if the quality of the water supply is not high. The feed formulation which is given is intended to be used at a conductivity of about 2.0 to 2.5mS/cm, depending on the quality of the water source. The irrigation rate should be set to give enough drainage through the slabs to prevent the slab solution conductivity from rising by more than 0.5mS/cm above that of the input solution. This may require overwatering by as much as 40% at some times, but an average drainage rate through the year of 20-25% may be adequate under most circumstances.

A standard pH of 5.0 is recommended for the feed solution and the aim should be to maintain a slab pH between 5.0 and 5.5. Earlier recommendations were for a slab pH of 5.8, but research has shown that at this level the crop can show quite a lot of leaf chlorosis on occasions and that this can be avoided by lowering the pH a little.

Roses have have a particular ability to influence the pH in the root zone, forcing it to drift either upwards or downwards, and under certain growing conditions it can be difficult to maintain the slab pH target. When the crop is growing most strongly, such as when it is approaching a flush, the slab pH is likely to rise. When the flush reaches maturity and harvesting begins there is a sudden change to pH reduction. If both the crop and the slab pH are conscientiously monitored and any developing trends are identified quickly enough, then corrective action can be taken early enough to reverse the trend before it produces any problems.

The usual options of changing the buffering capacity (bicarbonate content) of the feed or changing its ammonium level in the feed are available, although the former option will work more quickly than the latter. With experience it is possible to anticipate the change to pH reduction according to the stage of growth of the crop and to remove ammonium from the feed shortly before each flush reaches maturity.

## Winter management

One of the obvious benefits of growing roses in rockwool is the good winter production and quality which can be achieved. In low light areas it is usually economic to use supplementary lighting to keep the crop growing strongly through the winter. In areas which have particularly poor conditions in the winter months, such as Scandinavia, crop development at this time can be so slow that it may still be better to rest the crop through the winter. This in managed in rockwool by cutting back on the irrigation frequency and volume so that the slabs are barely moist.

It is essential that they are never allowed to dry back completely, though, because they will then be very difficult to re-wet. The strength of the input solution should be gradually lowered in advance of the winter rest so that the slab conductivity does not rise too high when the water content is reduced.

## CROP DISORDERS

Rose crops, especially certain varieties like Kiss and Eskimo, often show diffuse pale patches between the veins of the lower leaves and until recently it had not proved possible to identify the cause of these symptoms. It now seems that this is a form of magnesium deficiency, probably aggravated by high phosphorus levels in the plants. Leaf tissue analysis indicates that leaves which show these symptoms can contain one third as much magnesium and more than twice as much phosphorus as healthy leaves.

It seems that an excessive supply of phosphorus to the crop can often be the primary cause of these magnesium deficiency symptoms, often when a sudden reduction in the pH makes previously insoluble phosphates in the slab available to the roots. Other possible causes are an inadequate supply of magnesium in the nutrient solution, particularly during periods of strong growth, and poor root action induced by either insufficient aeration or low root temperatures. With susceptible varieties it is important to keep the slab pH stable, and to maintain a good level of magnesium in the slabs but not too much phosphorus.

## Root rot

A newly recognised root rot has started to show up in a number of rose crops in northern Europe in the last two years, often with devastating consequences. It has been found on soil-grown crops but has never been a serious problem until it started to become established in rockwool crops. It is caused by the fungal pathogen Gnomonia radicicola, which can spread rapidly throughout the root system to produce large numbers of wilting stems in an otherwise healthy crop.

Although the disease is still being investigated it seems that it is usually introduced on cuttings brought in from infected crops. The disease is therefore most likely to make an appearance during the first year after planting.

Gnomonia spreads very quickly through the nutrient solution so effective sterilisation of the solution in a recirculating system is vital. Chemical control measures will generally be needed to eradicate an established infection, but research is still under way to identify the most effective fungicides and application techniques.

# 17 Carnations

*Propagation. Layout and establishment. Irrigation and nutrition.*

The use of rockwool for carnations has never developed to the same extent as many other crops even though commercial crops have been successfully produced in rockwool since the late 1970's. The main advantage of using substrates for carnations has proved to be the relative freedom from soil-borne diseases like fusarium wilt and phialophora.

The need to move out of the soil came before inert substrates were widely considered as a commercial option, so peat growing media were chosen for the purpose. A lot of experience was then built up on the culture of carnations in peat so this production method has retained its popularity, although there is now a lot of interest in the use of rockwool and other inert substrates for this crop.

Trials comparing good soil-grown carnation crops with equivalent crops in peat or rockwool have generally shown only a small yield advantage in favour of the substrates, and this has to be offset against the higher production costs for soilless culture. This leaves freedom from soilborne disease as the obvious advantage of substrates. While this can be guaranteed at the start of the crop it does not always follow that diseases will not be introduced subsequently. Once into the system, diseases can spread rapidly in the ideal conditions of a well-managed substrate, particularly with recirculation of the nutrient solution.

Despite this, experience has shown that clean crops can be established and maintained in rockwool and that this can lead to higher yields and better quality than can be achieved in the soil. If the plants can then be kept disease-free a rockwool crop can remain in profitable production over a three-year cropping period rather than the traditional eighteen-month to two-year period which is more usual in the soil. The economics of the crop then swing back in favour of the use of rockwool.

## PLANT PROPAGATION

A number of different propagation techniques have been tried for carnations. Soil block cuttings do not establish well on to rockwool because the medium draws up water and salts from the rockwool slab and becomes too wet. Rooting the cuttings in perlite or a similar granulate material and placing bare-root cuttings directly on the surface of the growing slab through slits in the polyethylene wrap has been used successfully. This technique works well in dull conditions but it can be more difficult to achieve a good uniform establishment when the plants are under stress in hot sunny weather. Until recently most carnation growers used cuttings which had been rooted in rockwool granulate or in a mixture of rockwool and perlite. Now most carnation cuttings destined for planting into rockwool slabs are rooted in small rockwool multiblocks joined together during the propagation period, and separated into individual units for planting.

Whatever material is used to root the cuttings it should be wetted up with a weak nutrient solution, with a conductivity no higher than 0.8 to 1.2mS/cm and the pH adjusted to 5.5. The conductivity of the solution at the rooting stage should be as low as possible provided there is a minimal nutrient content available to the cuttings as they start to develop roots.

It is important to use the best quality water available at this stage and to use the higher end of the conductivity range only if the quality of the water is unavoidably poor. The cuttings are otherwise managed in the same way as cuttings intended for soil or peat culture, using tents and mist as necessary to minimise stress until the cuttings have a well established root system. Irrigation should be applied occasionally to the cuttings during rooting to maintain a supply of nutrients, even if generous quantities of water are reaching the substrate from the misting system.

## LAYOUT AND ESTABLISHMENT

For two- or three-year production it is advisable to use only high density rockwool to guarantee structural stability throughout the life of the crop. Wide slabs are most suited to the layout of this crop and either 60cm wide slabs or two 30cm slabs placed side by side are most commonly used. The standard slab depth of 7.5cm is adequate as carnations are shallow rooting, although some growers find that irrigation management is easier with 10cm deep slabs which have a greater air capacity after watering. The variable density slabs now available for cut flower production are giving very good results with carnations.

Profiling the glasshouse floor accurately is a job which cannot be neglected for this crop. The wide slabs have to be set on a slight but consistent slope to ensure that no areas of the slabs are at all waterlogged. Wet conditions will reduce the growth of the plants and greatly increase the risk of diseases becoming established.

Carnations benefit particularly from dry conditions above the slab surface and this can be helped by placing the heating pipes at slab height along the lower edge of the row of slabs. Warm air then moves up across the surface of the slab to reduce the humidity around the base of the stems and so protect against fungal infection entering at this level.

The same plant density is used for rockwool crops as for soil or peat crops, typically 30 to 35 plants/sq m.

It is not normally practicable to provide one irrigation nozzle per plant, but it is important to use as many nozzles as possible and to space them carefully over the surface of the slabs so that they wet up the whole slab volume as uniformly as possible. This usually means putting the nozzles closer together on the higher side of the slab and spacing them more widely on the lower side of the slab. A typical installation would have one nozzle for each four to six plants. The system will generally have to be able to supply one litre/hour/nozzle if the nozzle density is adequate but two-litre nozzles may be needed if the number of drips is less than one per five plants.

If bare root cuttings or cuttings raised in rockwool granulate are used they should be placed into shallow holes on the surface of the slabs. They should preferably be set at a shallow angle but not completely horizontal, so that as much as possible of the potential rooting area is in close contact with the surface of the slab. Placing them upright works well if the weather is continuously dull but the cuttings come under too much stress if the sun comes out. There is no problem with plants rooted in small rockwool cubes, which are simply placed upright on the surface of the slab, preferably in shallow planting holes.

The slabs should be wetted up in the usual way with a nutrient solution with a conductivity of about 1.5 to 2.0mS/cm. As discussed under 'Plant propagation' the higher end of the conductivity range should only be used if the water quality is mediocre.

The glasshouse humidity should be kept high during the establishment period and frequent small volumes of nutrient solution should be applied to the slabs to keep the top layer moist until the roots have moved well down into the slabs. Rooting into the slabs can be further encouraged by cutting the drainage slits for the wrapped slabs in two stages, first down to half way and then to the base a few days later. In this way the roots do not have to move too far down the slab to find an acceptable air to water ratio. Properly managed plants should be well established within two weeks, or even less in good growing conditions in the summer.

## IRRIGATION AND NUTRITION

As soon as the plants are established into the slabs the irrigation system should be set to give several applications a day, depending on the weather, each time allowing a drainage volume of about 15 to 20% of the total applied volume.

The nutrient solution strength should be set according to the growing conditions. When the crop is growing strongly in the summer the conductivity of the input solution should be no higher than about 2.0mS/cm. In poor light conditions in the winter the conductivity may be allowed to go as high as 3.0mS/cm. This can be achieved by raising the levels of the major nutrients in proportion in the feed. The formulation set out in the panel will give a conductivity of about 2.0mS/cm. Higher or lower conductivities should be produced by changing all of the major nutrients except phosphorus and ammonium, in proportion. The levels of micronutrients should not be changed.

The nutritional requirements of the crop change according to the stage of growth. It is not necessary to take account of this in an open system but a recirculating system may need occasional adjustments to be made to allow for these changes. Immediately after planting, for example, the rooted cuttings contain little calcium, but the vigorous growth they will be making over the next few weeks demands a lot of calcium so this nutrient tends to become depleted in the substrate. Later on, during a flush, the requirement for calcium falls to a low level so if the nutrient balance in the feed remains the same there will be a conspicuous increase in the accumulation of calcium in the slab solution. Potassium follows the opposite pattern, with low uptake during vegetative growth and an increased requirement during flower development.

### Input nutrient solution for carnations in rockwool

| | |
|---|---|
| $NH_4$-N | 7 ppm |
| $NO_3$-N | 200 ppm |
| P | 40 ppm |
| K | 280 ppm |
| Ca | 190 ppm |
| Mg | 30 ppm |
| | |
| Fe | 1.50 ppm |
| Cu | 0.05 ppm |
| Zn | 0.20 ppm |
| Mn | 0.55 ppm |
| B | 0.50 ppm |
| Mo | 0.05 ppm |

It is possible to anticipate these changes to keep the slab solution more constant. To do this, add an extra 30kg of calcium nitrate to each 1,000 litre batch of stock solution for the first two to three months of the new crop. During the period leading up to each flush replace 15kg of calcium nitrate in the basic formulation with the same amount of potassium nitrate. The need for these adjustments – and their effects – should of course be monitored by regular slab solution analysis.

# 18 Other ornamentals

*Gerberas. Bouvardias. Cymbidiums.*

Many other cut flower crops and other ornamental subjects are grown on rockwool, although not generally on the scale of roses and carnations. Gerbera, for example, does very well in rockwool, with reports of yield increases of up to 50% compared to traditional production in the soil.

## GERBERAS

Gerbera production in rockwool increased rapidly in importance during the early 1980's when the profitability of traditional growing methods fell as a result of rising fuel and labour costs. A few mistakes were made at first, but the developments of the last few years have produced a reliable and effective production method for this crop. Yields can be as much as 50% higher than a comparable soil-grown crop, and it is possible to extend a clean crop into two or even three years of worthwhile production.

The most important factors for good results with gerberas are adequate root zone temperatures and free drainage. With rockwool it is possible to optimise both of these factors easily and economically. It has also been demonstrated that the use of rockwool makes it possible to over-winter the crop with low air temperatures without any of the problems which occur when this is tried with soil crops.

### Glasshouse layout

The best way to use rockwool for gerberas is to raise the crop off the ground either on benches or on raised beds 20 to 25cm high, usually constructed from light concrete. This not only makes it much easier to harvest and work in the crop but also improves temperature and humidity management around the plants, reducing disease risks.

Bottom heat is essential, either through the benches themselves or alternatively through heating loops set into the upper surface of polystyrene slabs under the rockwool. It is also best if the glasshouse heating pipes can be raised to the height of the slabs and positioned along the edge of the rows.

Standard 15cm wide slabs are used, preferably with a depth of 10cm. These slabs carry a single row of plants. The slabs are arranged either in double rows or in a single row with double the plant density in the row.

An alternative way to use rockwool for gerberas is to plant individually into large growing blocks with a volume of about 6 litres. These are placed on to benches in the same way as slabs.

For either system an overall plant density of around 7 plants/sq m is generally used.

## Propagation and establishment

Micropropagation is now widely used to produce good quality disease-free planting material. Micropropagated plants are established into rockwool cubes and carefully weaned before they are moved into larger blocks.

Traditionally propagated plants from leaf cuttings are rooted directly into rockwool blocks. When these are placed on to the slabs there is enough total height from the base of the plant to the base of the slab to ensure good drainage and plenty of air in the root zone. Good irrigation management during the propagation stage is vital if the crop is to establish well. A healthy root system can only be achieved by keeping the air to water ratio within the root zone at an optimum level. The cuttings should not be set too deep in the blocks, the irrigation frequency should not be unnecessarily high, and there should always be unrestricted drainage from the base of the blocks.

Planting should be delayed until a good mat of white root is visible on the base of the blocks and until a slab temperature of at least 20C has been achieved. The irrigation nozzles should be positioned into the propagation blocks during the establishment period, but they should then be moved on to the slab surface to keep the crown of the plant as dry as possible.

Until the plants have rooted deep into the slabs the irrigation frequency should be high enough to avoid water stress, perhaps three or four times a day. Even then, some misting or light spraying over the crop may be needed during the spring or summer to keep the plants turgid until a strong root system has developed in the slab.

One advantage of rockwool is that the inevitable poor plants among the crop can be removed as soon as they are seen and replaced with new plants from the propagation area. A significant percentage of the plants may need to be replaced with some varieties, mainly because of disease infection of the planting material. This operation is much less practicable with a soil-grown crop and it produces much greater disturbance of the crop with consequently greater delays in production.

| Input nutrient solution for gerberas in rockwool | |
|---|---|
| NH$_4$-N | 7 ppm |
| NO$_3$-N | 170 ppm |
| P | 40 ppm |
| K | 210 ppm |
| Ca | 130 ppm |
| Mg | 25 ppm |
| Fe | 1.50 ppm |
| Cu | 0.10 ppm |
| Zn | 0.25 ppm |
| Mn | 0.50 ppm |
| B | 0.50 ppm |
| Mo | 0.05 ppm |

A typical nutrient solution for gerberas is given in the panel. It should be used at a conductivity of around 1.5mS/cm for propagation and for wetting up the slabs, rising to 2.0mS/cm when the crop is established in the growing house.

## Nutrition

There is some evidence that the precise nutritional requirement for gerberas differs according to the variety. Adjustments to the standard regime may need to be applied on the basis of experience, and it is easier to do this if only one variety is planted in each irrigation area. There may also be different irrigation frequency requirements according to variety.

Dutch feeding recommendations for gerberas were changed a few years ago, in particular to take into account the crop's sensitivity to ammonium. Gerberas will use any ammonium which is present in the slab solution to depress the solution pH, particularly when the crop is coming up to a flush, and this in turn can lead to nutritional imbalances. If there is any evidence of low slab pH levels, below about 5.0 to 5.5, the ammonium source should be omitted from the feed altogether.

A high ratio of iron to manganese should be maintained in the feed, because gerberas will suffer from iron deficiency if the slab manganese level gets too high. It may be necessary to reduce the feed manganese level down to 0.25 ppm if this happens, especially in a recirculation system.

### Resting period

The crop is usually rested through the winter by reducing the air temperature regime to just give protection from frost. During this stage the irrigation requirement of the crop is greatly reduced but it is important not to allow the conductivity of the slab solution to rise above 2.5mS/cm during the resting period, otherwise the crop will be slow to come into growth in the spring.

Heat should be gradually re-introduced so that the plants will produce a strong flush of flowers during February or early March. During active growth the over-watering rate should be high enough to ensure that the slab solution conductivity is never more than 0.5mS/cm above that of the input solution. This may require 30% or even 40% over-watering on occasions.

### BOUVARDIAS

Bouvardias are becoming quite a popular crop in Holland and they do particularly well in rockwool. One of the biggest advantages of using substrates for bouvardia, apart from the greater yield potential, is that it is possible to avoid the nematode problems which plague soil-grown crops. They are grown as a year-round crop either on single rows of 30cm wide slabs or on double rows of 15cm slabs. In either case, a slab depth of 7.5cm is adequate for this crop.

Substrate heating is generally used so that the crop can be economically kept in production through the winter. The plants can remain in production for up to five, or sometimes even seven years, so high density slabs are essential in order to retain the substrate structure throughout the cropping period. Unlike roses bouvardia has a fine root system which would not be able to cope with the reduced aeration conditions of rockwool which had lost its structural integrity.

Cuttings are rooted into rockwool blocks which have been wetted with a low conductivity nutrient solution, no higher than 1.5mS/cm, and these blocks are placed on to the slabs in the growing house as soon as they have made enough root.

**Input nutrient solution for bourvardias in rockwool**

| | |
|---|---|
| $NH_4$-N | 7 ppm |
| $NO_3$-N | 120 ppm |
| P | 40 ppm |
| K | 180 ppm |
| Ca | 120 ppm |
| Mg | 20 ppm |
| Fe | 1.50 ppm |
| Cu | 0.05 ppm |
| Zn | 0.25 ppm |
| Mn | 0.30 ppm |
| B | 0.30 ppm |
| Mo | 0.05 ppm |

A typical nutrient solution for bouvardias is shown in the panel. The slabs should be wetted up with this solution at a conductivity of between 1.8 and 2.2mS/cm, depending on the season and on the quality of the water supply. Once the crop is established in the slabs this solution should be used at a conductivity of around 1.8mS/cm in the summer, rising to about 2.2mS/cm for the winter period.

## CYMBIDIUMS

A lot of cymbidium orchids are still grown in peat-based media but there has been a steady move into rockwool and other inert substrates over the last few years and this trend is continuing. All orchids require a relatively high air capacity in the root zone and it has been found possible to produce ideal conditions with rockwool granulate. The sensitivity of cymbidiums to high salt levels in the substrate also supports the use of rockwool granulate, which is much easier to flush out effectively than peat-based materials.

Cymbidiums can only be successfully produced if good quality water is available or can be generated. The salt tolerance of the crop is so low that water sources which are adequate for other crops in rockwool may still not be suitable. The target should be to produce a nutrient solution with a total conductivity no higher than 1.0mS/cm. Since the bulk of this has to come from the nutrients required by the crop, the contribution from the water supply must be correspondingly low.

The nutritional requirements of cymbidiums in rockwool were established several years ago by grower trials co-ordinated from Aalsmeer Research Station in Holland. Cymbidiums proved to be particularly responsive to the supply of nitrogen and it was possible to demonstrate a progressive increase in the number of vegetative shoots and flower spikes which were produced as the nitrate nitrogen supply was increased from 25 ppm to 90 ppm.

This input solution should be used at the end of a flowering period while the crop is developing new growth. When the vegetative development of the crop is complete and flower initiation begins – usually around the end of March in northern Europe – an even weaker feed can be used to maximise flower production.

It is possible that giving only clear water at this stage would be satisfactory, but to err on the side of safety it is better to supply a nutrient solution at a conductivity of about 0.5 to 0.7mS/cm. This is where good water quality becomes especially important. If the conductivity of the water supply is even around 0.3mS/cm, which would be classified as excellent for most crops in substrates, there is very little margin for adding nutrients.

At the end of the summer the feed strength should be brought back to 1.0mS/cm until the end of the flowering period.

### Input nutrient solution for cymbidiums in rockwool

| | |
|---|---|
| $NH_4$-N | 14 ppm |
| $NO_3$-N | 90 ppm |
| P | 30 ppm |
| K | 125 ppm |
| Ca | 70 ppm |
| Mg | 20 ppm |
| | |
| Fe | 0.50 ppm |
| Cu | 0.03 ppm |
| Zn | 0.25 ppm |
| Mn | 1.00 ppm |
| B | 0.25 ppm |
| Mo | 0.05 ppm |

*The amount of ammonium nitrogen supplied in the nutrient solution should be adjusted to keep the pH in the rockwool slab close to the optimum value of around 5.5*

# Appendix

## *Rockwool in North America*

*The author is grateful to **Douglas H Marlow**, Grodania representative for Canada and author of 'Greenhouse crops in North America – a practical guide to stonewool culture', for much of the material in this appendix. The pesticide and other chemical recommendations given here are specific to North America and may not be permitted or appropriate in other growing areas.*

Rockwool has been available in the USA and in Canada for well over a decade now but it is only in the last few years that it has started to become firmly established in commercial horticulture. Most of the intensive production of vegetables under protection in North America is concentrated in the northern USA and in Canada. Already more than a half of all the greenhouse vegetable crops in Canada are grown on rockwool, and considerable expansion is still occurring in British Columbia and Ontario.

In the USA California has started to move into rockwool in a big way for the production of high quality cut flowers, especially roses and gerbera. In this State there is already a lot of pressure from the environmental lobby which will add impetus to the move out of the soil and into closed growing systems.

North American growing conditions are much more varied than those in Europe, with climatic zones from sub-tropical to northern temperate, and with altitudes from sea-level up to several thousand metres. These geographical differences result in much wider ranges in a number of environmental factors, such as temperature, light intensity, daylength and humidity, than growers in northern Europe would expect to encounter. This does not affect the principles of growing in rockwool or other substrates but it does require a broader base of specific crop culture recommendations and cropping schedules.

Rockwool can be obtained in North America in high, standard and low density slabs for vegetable and flower production. The high density slabs, which are mainly used for long-term crops like roses, are the same as those which are marketed in Europe, having a density of about 80kg/cu m. The standard density product, which is similiarly suitable for steam sterilisation and reuse, has a

---

*In many parts of North America acrylic or polycarbonate materials are used extensively for cladding protected cropping structures in place of glass. And in Ontario, home to the most concentrated area of protected cultivation in North America, more than a third of the structures are covered with double skinned polyethylene. For this reason the term 'greenhouse' is more appropriate than 'glasshouse' when discussing North American horticulture.*

density of 60–70kg/cu m, and the low density single-season slab has a density of 50 to 55kg/cu m. The full range of high density propagation plugs, cubes and blocks is also available, as are rockwool granulates.

## GREENHOUSE PREPARATION

Very few pesticides are licensed in North America for use on edible crops grown under protection. This means that all available means of avoiding contact between the crop and a potential source of infection must be used. Any contact between the growing substrate, or any equipment or materials which come into contact with it, and the soil either within or outside the greenhouse must be prevented to avoid the introduction of soil-borne fungal or bacterial pathogens and pests such as nematodes.

The greenhouse floor must be completely covered with black/white 4 or 6 mil co-extruded polyethylene placed white side up, or with an opaque material of similar thickness. All equipment should be surface sterilised with a 10% bleach solution, which should also be used in foot baths at all entry points into the growing house.

### Sterilants and disinfectants

A number of sterilants and disinfectants are available in North America to aid hygiene between crops. Naled (Dibrome) is particularly effective for insect elimination at the end of a crop after all edible products have been harvested but before the crop residue is cleared out. Subject to local authority restrictions, naled is used at a rate of 30ml/100cu m (4 litres/acre), and is applied either as a low volume spray or by vapourising it on the heating pipes or any suitable hot surface. A minimum air temperature of 25C is needed for 12 hours after treatment to maximise the effect of this treatment. If treatment is delayed beyond September, and spider mites have gone into their winter resting stage, naled will only be effective if the air temperature can be raised to about 35C.

The greenhouse structure can be washed down and surface sterilised with 10% chlorine bleach, formaldehyde, gluteraldehyde or quarternary ammonium chloride salts (Q-salts). Formaldehyde is effective, but it is harmful to users, so it can only be used under controlled conditions. Q-salts, which are available in a number of commercial formulations, are becoming the most popular material for greenhouse cleaning. They have no residual effect, but they are effective against a wide range of pathogens.

### Closed systems

In many areas of North America there is as yet no specific requirement to protect the environment by using a closed recirculating system with rockwool or any other growing medium. This is likely to change very soon, however, and growers are strongly advised to install at least a closed system, even if full recirculation is not carried out. This will provide the basis for total containment if and when it is required, and will give valuable experience in the operation of such installations in the meantime. If the quality of the water supply and other factors make recirculation a viable option then this should be considered from the start.

In cooler climatic areas slabs which are to be positioned at floor level should be placed on to thin strips of polystyrene, 0.5 to 1.0cm thick, rolled out along each row, to provide thermal insulation against low soil temperatures. For better temperature management in colder areas the slabs should be heated from a pipe loop set into the top surface of a thicker polystyrene slab.

## IRRIGATION AND NUTRITION

Most ground water sources in North America require acidification to reduce their bicarbonate alkalinity content. However there are some water sources, particularly in the north eastern USA, that have a very low bicarbonate content. In this case they should be treated in the same way as rainwater, adding potassium bicarbonate into either the water storage tanks or the fertiliser stock solution to provide some pH buffering.

### Light levels

The extreme climatic conditions which are encountered in some areas of North America require some modification to the feeding and irrigation regimes used in Europe. In particular the very high light levels which occur in the summer months in the south are likely to be combined with low air humidities in the greenhouse whenever full ventilation is applied during the day.

Under these conditions the conductivity level in the rockwool slabs can be rapidly increased by the volume of water being taken up by the crop. This can be prevented by increasing the number of irrigation cycles per day while keeping the volume applied on each occasion constant. The feed conductivity should at the same time be lowered to the minimum level consistent with the crop's nutritional requirements. This may be as low as 1.0mS/cm if the water quality is very high, otherwise around 1.5mS/cm. It is important that this conductivity should include an adequate contribution from fertilisers, and that it should not consist solely of the salts present in the water source.

The opposite effect can occur in the winter months in areas where the light levels are frequently poor and where outside air temperatures are so low that no ventilation can be given. Under these conditions the humidity in the greenhouse will always be high, and the crop may develop too much vegetative growth. The slab conductivity should be increased to prevent this, and this can be achieved by a combination of higher strength feeding and a reduction in the frequency of watering.

## Solarisation

An option for sterilising rockwool slabs for re-use which is available in many areas of North America but which is seldom considered in northern Europe is solarisation. This is a long-term heat treatment process which uses the heat of the sun, built up under a polyethylene cover, to kill disease pathogens.

Even in areas of the highest light intensity solarisation can take several weeks so it is best used by having two sets of rockwool slabs, one in production and the other under treatment for the following season. The slabs are stacked on slabs in the same way as for steam sterilisation, covered with 4 mil polyethylene and left exposed to the sun, either in the open or preferably in a greenhouse. The aim is to generate a temperature throughout the stack of 80C or above for long enough to complete the sterilisation process.

## VEGETABLE CROP PRODUCTION

The total greenhouse vegetable production area in North America was calculated in 1993 to be 475ha, or nearly 1,200 acres. Of this total 60% of the area was used for tomato production, 30% for cucumbers and most of the rest for peppers or lettuce. Most of the tomatoes grown at present are beefsteak types. Apart from rockwool, sawdust, perlite and peat mixes are all used as media for this crop.

In general the nutritional requirements for vegetable crops in North America are similar to those for crops produced in Europe but in the areas of highest light intensity, specifically Southern California, Colorado, Idaho and Alberta, the crop is likely to show an increased demand for some of the micronutrients. Copper, iron, manganese and zinc are all involved in the process of photosynthesis, so as the daylength increases and the maximum light intensity starts to rise in the spring the uptake of these nutrients starts to increase. The levels of all of these nutrients in the slab should be gradually built up towards the end of the winter period to anticipate this extra demand.

## P&D control

Biological pest control in vegetable crops is widely used in North America. The parasitic wasp Encarsia formosa is effective for whitefly control provided the greenhouse temperature can be kept at 22C or above. Phytoseiulus persimilis is used to control the two-spotted spider mite, sometimes in combination with the pesticide fenbutatin-oxide where the use of this material is permitted. Western Flower Thrips on cucumbers is treated with Amblyseius cucumeris and A barkeri. The former is less effective under low light and low temperature conditions, but is otherwise the more effective of the two predators. In high temperatures Amblyseius californicus is a good option against Thrips urticae, as it will tolerate the heat better and survive well at low host densities.

Orius species, the 'pirate bugs', are also commonly used against a range of insect pests, but they will hibernate in low light conditions so they can only be used effectively during the summer.

Powdery mildew is a big problem on rockwool cucumbers in North America. The addition of potassium metasilicate to the feed, which is sometimes recommended as a way of reducing crop susceptibility to powdery mildew in Europe, has met with only limited success, and growers have had to rely on a combination of humidity control and sulphur applications.

Pythium can quickly devastate greenhouse cucumber crops in North America, where there are no chemicals registered for use on edible crops and growers have to rely on good crop hygiene.

## High-light penalties

A lot of the tomato area is grown on a two-crop system to avoid the high temperatures and low prices which commonly occur in June and July. Where crops are grown through the year in high light areas they need to be shaded in the summer to reduce plant stress. Partial shading is recommended when the light intensity outside the greenhouse reaches about 600W/sq m, and full shading, with 25 to 30% light reducing cloth, should be used at outdoor light intensities of 850W/sq m and above. Crops grown through the summer in this type of climate may need to be watered at no more than half hour intervals at peak demand, but at a minimum conductivity to avoid rapid build-up of salts in the rockwool.

The ratio between potassium and nitrogen in the rockwool slabs can be used to help both tomato and pepper crops cope with the high summer light levels and temperatures that occur in central Canada and the south west United States. By reducing the availability of potassium and increasing the nitrogen supply, both crops can be encouraged to produce longer and larger leaves. This extra foliage not only contributes to the overall vigour of the crop by increasing the photosynthetic area, it also gives more shade to the crop and protects the fruit from sun scald.

If shading screens are available, peppers should be shaded rather more heavily than tomatoes, starting with partial shade at a light intensity outside the greenhouse of about 500W/sq m.

## Lettuce regime

The technique of lettuce production in a combination of rockwool cubes and NFT troughs is popular in Canada. Using this system each crop can be ready to harvest five to 10 weeks after planting, depending on the season. It is important to encourage as much calcium uptake as possible by lettuce, especially when the greenhouse humidity is high, to minimise tip burn. The calcium uptake and distribution in the crop can also be improved if the circulating nutrient solution is heated to a few degrees above the air temperature.

## FLOWER CROP PRODUCTION

Roses are the most important cut flower crop in rockwool in both Canada and the USA. The switch from soil to rockwool has been shown to greatly improve winter flower quality, particularly in areas with poor winter light. Among the most popular varieties of rose for planting on rockwool at present are Kardinal, Samantha, Bridal Pink and Bridal White.

Most growers now use own-root cuttings following the success which has been achieved with this material in Europe, but a few still prefer to use grafted plants.

A similar range of plant density is used to that employed by European producers (see chapter 16), but there are regional variations. Areas with the highest overall light levels such as Southern California and the south west United States can successfully use densities as low as 4 plants/sq m. Some areas of northern and central USA and Canada, which have particularly low light levels in the winter, need a density of 10 or 11 plants/sq m to maximise production.

Gerberas are also well established as a cut flower crop in both the USA and Canada, and many growers have already taken advantage of the better growing conditions and therefore higher production which can be achieved by moving out of the soil and into rockwool. Substrate warming is widely used, particularly in regions with low winter temperatures, where the advantage of more vigorous plant growth, higher yields and longer stems can be combined with the more economical use of heating fuel.

Supplementary lighting is often provided for gerberas in the winter, and in this case, or in conditions of high natural light levels, the uptake of some nutrients, especially nitrogen, potassium, copper, zinc and iron, can increase dramatically. The feeding programme should be modified to anticipate these changes before they deplete the levels of these nutrients in the slabs.

## TERMINOLOGY

While most North American growers will recognise all of the terminology used in this book, there arc one or two terms which may not be universally recognised.

The point at which the irrigation system delivers feed to the crop, known in Europe as the 'nozzle', 'drip' or 'dripper', may sometimes be referred to as the 'emitter'. Similarly the 'diluter', which combines concentrated fertiliser solution and water to produce a dilute nutrient solution, may be better known by some growers as a 'proportioner' or 'injector'.

As in Europe the terms 'stonewool' and 'rockwool' are now accepted to be more or less synonymous despite earlier debate about trade marks and proprietary names, but while most growers in Europe opt for 'rockwool' as a generic description of the material, North American growers more often use the term 'stonewool'.

The total salt content of water or a nutrient solution is universally measured by its electrical conductivity, but there are two alternative abbreviations for this. In North America the accepted abbreviation is 'EC', for electrical conductivity. In the UK and in many other areas the term 'cf' is preferred, standing for conductivity factor. In either case the conductivity is measured in the same units, milliSiemens per centimeter, often simplified to mS/cm or just mS, although to confuse the issue some publications refer to conductivity in microSiemens, or µS. This should not be a serious problem, because 1mS is the same as 1,000 µS, and the difference between the two is so great that it should be obvious which scale is being used.

The content of nutrients and other ions in a solution is described in the USA and Canada in terms of ppm, or parts per million. This unit is also used in many other countries, including the UK, although the alternative unit, milligrams per litre (mg/l) is also widely used in Europe. This is not a problem, because the two units give identical values. 1 ppm is exactly the same as 1mg/litre. A bigger problem is the preferred use of a completely different unit in Holland, from where a lot of technical information on the use of rockwool comes. The Dutch recognise and use the molar system, referring to the nutrient content of a solution in terms of millimoles per litre (mmol/litre). If these units are encountered, the panel in chapter 11 (p78) shows how to convert to mmol/litre to ppm for each nutrient or other ion.

One difference between North America and Europe which can sometimes present problems is in the strength and nutrient content of some fertilisers and related materials. It is never safe to assume that a material which is referred to only by its chemical name has the same formulation in one country as in another. For example there are various ranges of micronutrients with quite different levels of the active ingredient, and the availability of these can differ from country to country. If in doubt, find out the percentage content of the material which is being recommended and compare it to what is present in the material available locally. Within this book no assumptions have been made about the formulation of any fertiliser to which a reference has been made.

Finally, there are now fewer problems with the standard units of measure, as most horticultural publications in North America have adopted the standard international units such as litres, metres, square metres and hectares, and these are becoming recognised and used within the horticultural industry.

Conversion between international units and local units like pints, gallons [US or UK], yards and acres can be made where necessary, but is now seldom needed. The conversion factors listed in the panel may be helpful.

## Approximate conversion factors

| To convert from: | To: | Multiply by: |
|---|---|---|
| UK gallons | US gallons | 1.2 |
| litres | US gallons | 0.26 |
| litres | UK gallons | 0.22 |
| centimeters | inches | 0.4 |
| metres | yards | 1.1 |
| square metres | square yards | 1.2 |
| hectares | acres | 2.5 |
| pounds | kilograms | 0.45 |
| ounces | grams | 28.4 |

# *Index*

## Chemical symbols commonly used in substrate culture

### Major nutrients

| | |
|---|---|
| $NO_3$-N | Nitrogen, in nitrate form |
| $NO_3$ | Nitrate |
| $NH_4$-N | Nitrogen, in ammonium form |
| $NH_4$ | Ammonium |
| N | Nitrogen in any form |
| $P_2O_5$ | Phosphate* |
| P | Phosphorus |
| $K_2O$ | Potash* |
| K | Potassium |
| Ca | Calcium |
| Mg | Magnesium |
| Na | Sodium |
| Cl | Chloride (or chlorine) |

*The terms 'phosphate' and 'potash' are seldom used in crop nutrition today, 'phosphorus' and 'potassium' being preferred*

### Minor nutrients

| | |
|---|---|
| Fe | Iron |
| Cu | Copper |
| Zn | Zinc |
| Mn | Manganese |
| B | Boron |
| Mo | Molybdenum |
| Si | Silicon |

### Others

| | |
|---|---|
| $HCO_3$ | Bicarbonate |
| $CO_3$ | Carbonate |
| $SO_4$-S | Sulphur in sulphate form |

*'Minor nutrients' are those which are needed in relatively small amounts. They are also referred to as 'micronutrients' or 'trace elements'*